Bioenergetics

Part 1: Healing Trauma & Conditioning

by Devaraj Sandberg

First Edition, 2020

The moral rights of the author have been asserted

ISBN: 978-0-9957708-9-8

Published by Devaraj Nick Sandberg

Illustrations by Victor Nassar
Cover Design by Leonie Isaacs

All enquiries to devaraj227@gmail.com
Author's Website: https://bioenergetics.org.uk

Contents

Introduction

There's one idea, hidden deep within the human mind, which seems to exert an eternal pull on our psyche. It attracts us in all sorts of different ways and forms. The idea is that there exists a "Grand Cause" for all that ails us. The notion that all of our dramas, struggles and failings can be traced back to one original diversion or disconnection from our true nature.

Some try to make it a political thing, something on the outside. If we only had the right government, the right leader, the right system, then we would be okay. Some try to make it a religious thing. If only we had the right god. If only everyone believed in the same god.

But, personally, I believe that increasing numbers of us have begun to realize that the problem may not be on the outside. We have ceased blaming something going on around us for our personal struggles. We have begun to take the brave first steps in self-honesty. Not blaming ourselves, but still taking responsibility. We have begun to recognise the true nature of the "Grand Cause" of all human issues. For those brave souls, I have written this book.

When I was a kid, back in the 60s, there was a programme on TV called "Journey to the Center of the Earth." It was based on the novel by Jules Verne and, as I recall, it starred Doug McClure. A group of intrepid explorers had found a hole in the earth's surface and they were beginning its exploration. Unlike usual such holes, it did not peter out quickly into a dead end. It went deeper. And deeper. What supported this group of explorers, as they delved deeper into the unknown, was the knowledge that one person had travelled this path before them, a character known as Arne Saknussemm. Every now and again he had carved his initials, "A.S.," into a rock. Finding these carvings reassured the explorers that they were on the right path - the journey to the centre of the Earth. I loved this programme and watched it every week.

When, in my late 30s, I began to get involved in intense therapeutic work I found myself in a similar situation to Doug and his friends on TV. I began to realise that, despite my considerable knowledge of the world, I actually knew very little about who I was. I had simply spent my life looking out at the world and learning about how it seemed to work. Trying to find ways to get my needs met. Somewhere I had dismissed the notion of self-examination, believing it was "better not to look." Better to get on with life.

As the journey I was on with group therapy threw me deeper and deeper into my unexamined depths, I found myself incredibly grateful for the support and guidance of the therapists I was working with. They had been there before me and could show me the way forwards when I was lost in fear and confusion. They hadn't learned it all from a book. They had actually been there, where I was now.

Make no mistake, when you work with the muscle system and fascia of the body, you are working at what is likely the deepest level of the human psyche. You are led into your depths as the muscles open up through Bioenergetics practice and release the past. I am happy and grateful to be able to give you some guidance on this journey. Despite what your mind will tell you at times, you can do it. With some support and guidance, you can make it. You can have the life you want. You can have the friendships and relationships you want. You can have the future you want. All it takes is the courage to face yourself on a deep level. And to take in positivity as you let go of the past.

It can seem at times like a long and arduous journey. But the good thing is, as I'm happy to report, your life gets better along the way. We can do it. You can do it.

The Grand Cause of all Human Problems

The human brain has the capacity to repress feelings.

This simple statement points directly to the cause of pretty much the whole catalogue of human woes, on both a personal and planetary level. Illness, neurosis, depression, conflict, injustice, gender battles, famine, eco-catastrophe - believe it or not, our ability to repress lies at the heart of it all. In fact, nearly every issue which besets our civilization, right from when our body hair decreased and we began to walk upright, can be traced right back to our capacity to repress feelings. It is the Grand Cause of all our Suffering.

As we evolved from more simple primates into human beings, our frontal lobes increased vastly in size and complexity. This happened as the ability to work with information became more and more favoured.

Along with our improved ability to create useful models of how the world around us functioned, came an expansion of our capacity to create ideas of who we were, and to interact with others through this "self-image." The human personality took off.

I am this type of person. I like this type of music. I don't like this type of clothing. I agree with this political or philosophical perspective. I have had these experiences. I don't agree with the people over there. I am attracted to this kind of person. As our frontal lobes increased in processing power, so we could create increasingly complex notions of who we were.

In many ways, this expansion of our frontal lobes, and the changes it brought, was the backbone of human civilisation. But it came at a huge price. Just as we became able to create complex notions of who we were, we inevitably increased our capacity to lie to ourselves and others about what was going on inside of us. We began to have the option to live via "a persona," rather than be honest and real.

Many of us have learned to live through a carefully curated self-image, designed to appear perfect and attractive to those we aspired to be, or to be with. However, in order to do so, we had to repress those parts of us which didn't fit in with this image of who we should be. We created an unconscious repository of unwanted aspects of ourselves which we endeavoured to keep hidden from view.

We can hide what is really going on inside and keep wearing a mask - on our face and in our behaviour. We can choose to show others that which we want them to see, and anything else we can try to keep hidden. But from this deception arises pretty much every issue which besets our culture. It is the act of keeping so many feelings repressed, of constantly having to hold down so much emotion, that leads to all the problems.

Because, although the feelings are repressed, they have not gone away. They sit, bound into our muscle system and fascia, and exert a constant charge within our psyche. This charge creates an anxiety, a sense of unease within us, that we do not wish to examine for fear that our carefully prepared self-image might fall apart.

Thus, we succumb to any strategy which can keep this underlying anxiety at bay. We learn to judge those who trigger our repressed feelings, convincing ourselves that the problem is on the outside. We may become depressed, our brain simply squashing all feelings down to avoid the specific feeling it seeks to avoid. We may become addicts of any behaviour which can keep our anxiety at bay, even if only for a short while.

Because buying stuff makes us feel good for a short while, we become the willing slaves of consumer culture. Because drugs and alcohol help us keep our anxieties down for a while, we allow ourselves to consume them regularly, despite damage to our health and relationships. Because we are so desperate to keep anxiety away, we willingly submit to a monotonous, comfort-driven life. It all comes down to feelings and our brain's capacity to repress them.

Blaming ourselves for this repression, beating ourselves up, will not help us. It is actually just another strategy for self-avoidance. Many of the brain's mechanisms to repress feelings take place unconsciously, meaning it really isn't our fault that this repression is taking place.

The way forward is to progressively take responsibility for who we are - and to stop blaming the outside. We need to embark upon a journey of personal change, seeking any support we need along the way.

In this chapter, I shall be looking more closely at why we repress feelings, the physical and mental effects of this repression, and most importantly what we can do about it.

Bioenergetics removes the blocks. This book is not about telling you who to be, what to do with your life, or how to get love. It's not about adding stuff to who you think you are. It's about giving you the tools to remove the blocks from your own being, allowing you to become a happy, successful and authentic individual. This is more of an undoing, rather than a learning.

So, What Do We Mean by Repression?

On a psychological level, repression is the act of putting off feeling something. The events of our lives create emotional responses within us. We feel happiness, pain, anger, jealousy, love and much more. However, it appears that the brain has a programme to "offset" emotional responses in certain situations. If the brain believes it would be dangerous to feel the impact of a certain emotional stimulus, perhaps because we are still at an early age of development, then it can store away this feeling, keeping it out of our conscious awareness.

We can imagine an animal needing to not feel something, right in the moment, in order to survive a dangerous situation. So we can understand how useful this capacity to offset emotional responses would have been to our evolutionary ancestors.

Perhaps you had the experience of feeling simply numb in a situation that you knew should be provoking intense emotions within you. Maybe it was only after a while that you began to feel the intensity of what happened.

The brain constantly monitors what is going on around us, and has the ability to automatically repress feelings if it judges a situation potentially traumatic. This is a protective response that happens predominantly in early childhood, when our brain is still developing. But it can also happen later on, in extreme situations such as war, violence or abandonment.

This "trauma response" is invariably unconscious, meaning it happens outside of our conscious control. But, trauma aside, there is also another category of situations where we learn to repress feelings and do so willingly. These situations we can label as "conditioning."

Let's take a closer look at these two categories of situation - trauma and conditioning.

Trauma

The word "trauma" refers to any extreme, emotionally-provocative event that might take place in our life. Often, we associate trauma with early childhood, perhaps an experience of abandonment or an accident that befell us. But trauma can also happen later on. Perhaps we lost a loved one or were in a car accident. Maybe we were involved in a war or other major conflict. Indeed, one of the first psychiatrists to write about trauma and the body, Bessel van der Kolk, was not studying small infants but rather treating veterans of the Vietnam war.

Trauma refers to any very powerful life event, where all or most of the emotional impact is repressed. There are two general categories of events which commonly create trauma - withdrawal wounds and invasion wounds.

Withdrawal wounds are when we expect someone or something to be there, and they are not. Abandonment of the child by one or both parents is a common type of withdrawal trauma.

As little babies, we are genetically predisposed to expect our parents to be there when we need them. When this need is not fully met, then it is common for us to lock away the pain of this sense of abandonment, it being too much to feel and express in the moment. Withdrawal wounds tend to leave a residue of emotional pain within the body.

Invasion wounds are the opposite of withdrawal wounds. These occur when someone crosses our boundaries without our consent. Invasion wounding can be overt, as in sexual abuse or severe physical punishing. It can also be more subtle, such as you not being allowed to simply "be yourself" while growing up, often the result of an overly controlling parent. Once again, it is common for these types of wounds to leave traces in the muscle system. Invasion wounds tend to leave a residue of anger in the body.

Conditioning

Conditioning is the act of creating a personality in order to fit in with society or a social group.

Humans are not solitary creatures by nature. We all naturally develop social needs, which we will seek to get met from others. Pretty much everyone will experience three different types of social need, which usually manifest in the following order…

- Firstly, we want **friends**.
- Then we seek **lovers** or a partner.
- Finally, we look for a **job** or a role within society.

What we invariably learn is that we need to be a certain way to get these needs met. Or, more accurately, we need to appear to be a certain way to the outside world. We learn that to fit in with society and get our needs met, we must regulate our personality. So, we learn to construct what psychologists call a "persona" - a front through which we can interact with the world.

When I was growing up in the seventies, young men learned that in order to fit in with other guys, and be attractive to women, you needed to appear to be strong. It was not okay to be vulnerable. It was certainly not okay to cry, except in rare circumstances (such as England losing at football). It was okay to be angry and violent, but not to show weakness or vulnerability. So I learned to repress emotional pain, to keep it hidden beneath a facade of low-level hostility that I put out to the world.

Similarly, at that time, it was not okay for women to be angry, to really take a position for themselves. In order to fit in with other women, and to be attractive to men, most women learned to repress their anger and to appear passive. It was okay to collapse weeping, but not okay to say "no" to something that you did not want in your life.

These are just examples taken from my own adolescence. You may well have been brought up in an environment where different social pressures were applied to you. But the underlying message for us all is the same - if we want to get our needs met, we need to exert control over our natural emotionality.

There is actually an organ of the brain whose job it is to regulate our personality. It's called the prefrontal cortex (PFC) and it has immense power. Time and again, I've witnessed people frozen with fear when the possibility of changing a behaviour presented itself. There is a reason for this. It happens because, during our evolutionary development, the consequences of us not fitting in were invariably extreme, in fact frequently catastrophic.

Not fitting in with the tribe or group, in a hunter-gatherer society - or in primate culture - would result in ostracism. If we were expelled from the group, our chances of survival were low. Thus, the prefrontal cortex has immense power, and we instinctively develop considerable fear around the slightest change in our personality.

How Repression Manifests Physically

We have looked above at why emotions sometimes aren't felt in the moment but instead stored away. Traumatic events or times we've allowed ourselves to be socially conditioned can both result in repression. Now let's take a look at how this repression manifests physically.

Back in the 1920s, Austrian-born psychiatrist, Wilhelm Reich, discovered a common thread between repressed emotions, personality and body posture. One of the things that he uncovered was that how posture develops over time is primarily related to the conditions of our childhood.

People brought up in a certain way, subjected to certain forms of trauma and conditioning, developed characteristic personalities as a means to keep repressed emotions held within. At the same time, the muscles and fascia of their bodies became distorted and formed a posture which, likewise, reflected the influences of early life trauma and conditioning.

Let's take a closer look at our muscles. Healthy muscles are toned and have a natural resilience. They can be put under considerable stress, but will naturally return to a relaxed, toned condition when the stress is over. However, few muscles are in this healthy, toned state.

Muscles that are holding the past develop what are known as "holding patterns" - areas of unnatural rigidity that don't relax even when no stress is present. They also develop "dead zones" - areas where all the toning appears to have literally fallen out of the muscles, rather as though they had been "disowned" by the body.

So, to sum up, the act of repressing feelings creates holding patterns and dead zones in the muscles of different areas of our body. This is why our posture says a lot about our childhood and any trauma or conditioning that we are still carrying.

Instead of vibrating with life energy, our natural state, many of us struggle to just get through the day. We no longer feel our bodies properly, for we've been using them as a dumping ground for unwanted feelings. When asked to describe how their body feels, most people report sensing only a dull, relatively unchanging mass. This lack of vital sensation is not natural and is purely the result of repression.

The therapeutic technique that Reich and his students pioneered was to release these unnatural patterns of holding and limpness in the muscles through body movement and deep breathing. He discovered that the effects of trauma and conditioning could be removed in this manner. As this work developed over time, it eventually led to Bioenergetics.

The Areas of the Body Mostly Affected

Having looked at why the repression of feelings takes place, and how it affects the body, we might now be interested to learn which areas of the body are most affected.

The answer is strangely straightforward. When thinking about making a good impression, most of us are primarily concerned that the front of our body looks good. We want to have a smiling, attractive face, a prominent chest and a firm stomach.

Thus, when considering where to hide all the feelings that don't fit in with our carefully constructed persona, the prefrontal cortex selects the back of the body. The lower back, the backs of the legs, the shoulders and the neck are the main areas that bear the brunt of our need to look good. The muscles in our lower back are so heavily used as a "dumping ground," that most people, by the time they reach their twenties, can no longer feel their lower back.

Why Repression Stops Us Moving Forwards in Life

Holding patterns and dead zones are the two physical manifestations of repressed emotions. They appear very different, but it is useful to consider them both as acting like a "charge" within the body and mind. Whether a muscle is unnaturally tense, or whether there has been a withdrawal of sensation from a muscle, the effect is the same. The body has become "charged" with the past. Our life energy has become bound up in our muscle system. If we can release this charge we will feel more alive.

Since the 1960s, more and more people have been embarking on a process of personal change. Many are dropping old, limited views of what they can achieve and are embracing new ideas and possibilities. Our world often seems to be on the verge of seismic shifts in human behaviour and increasing numbers of people are signing up, wanting to get on board.

But now that this global movement is a few decades down the line, what is becoming clear is that it is actually not so easy to create change. Many report having a burst of enthusiasm, rapidly followed by falling back into a rut. Old habits seem to die hard. This repeated falling back can also induce more negativity and a tendency to beat oneself up.

I've heard of a follow-up study that was carried out one month after a 3-day seminar led by a world-famous motivational guru in London. Everyone came out of the workshop pumped up to create massive change in their lives. However, the study revealed that over 98% of those who attended actually were back where they started just one month later. Why would this be the case? The answer relates to repression and to this "charge" from the past.

As noted above, repressed emotions act like an electrical charge bound up in our muscle system. There is an area of the brain, often known as the reptilian brain or brain stem, whose job it is to release this charge. How it goes about doing this is to cause us to be drawn into situations that, on some level, resemble the situation that created the charge in the first place. Maybe it's a certain type of relationship with our boss at work. Or perhaps a certain type of man or woman to whom we seem to be constantly attracted, regardless of how many times we learn that they are not good for us.

The stored charge creates a conflict between our higher mind, our prefrontal cortex, and our brain stem. The higher, thinking mind wants to go for a good future - a suitable partner who will nourish us and harmonious relationships at work. But the brain stem keeps trying to drag us back into the past. Its job is to get us to fully experience repressed emotions and thus release them.

The way out of this conflict is to take control of the situation. We need to take steps to release this charge from the muscle system ourselves. When our muscles regain their natural resilience and the charge is gone, then creating healthy change will be much easier. You will no longer find yourself dragged back into old conflicts. Old mental patterns that do not serve you will not necessarily disappear overnight but there will no longer be a charge underneath them, holding them in place. Thus, you will find making healthy choices much easier. Changing your life will become a reality.

What Is Bioenergetics?

What is Bioenergetics? Simply put, Bioenergetics is a body-movement therapy specifically intended to remove the effects of repression from the body. In this it is unique. These days there are many types of therapy that work with the body - Pilates, Alexander Technique, Rolfing, Myofascial Release - to name but a few. There are also many other wonderful gym workouts, yoga sequences, and dance workshops you can explore. But only Bioenergetics has this specific intention. Only Bioenergetics is there to get the charge out of the muscle system and fascia.

History

The word "Bioenergetics" was coined by the American psychologist, Alexander Lowen, back in the 1950s. He developed his own school of body-oriented psychotherapy, Bioenergetic Analysis, from the work of Wilhelm Reich, under whom he studied in the 1940s.

However, personally, I hesitate to ascribe the whole of Bioenergetics solely to Lowen and related therapists. Many of the postures you will find in this book seem to have their origins in earlier tribal cultures and Shamanic groups from places as diverse as the Americas and Siberia. Inevitably, little is known for sure, nor can be proven, but I want to acknowledge the wisdom of tribal peoples in this field.

That said, let's briefly cover what is recorded about the history of this innovative Body-based Therapy.

When Wilhelm Reich fled the Nazis and came to America, he brought with him his revelatory ideas about the relationship between the body and the mind. He attracted much attention amongst the more open-minded psychologists of the day. His ideas of trauma, of charge, of the therapeutic value of sex and of "life energy" attracted many adherents throughout the 1940s.

However, like many brilliant thinkers, Reich wasn't without his own personality flaws. His occasional over-focussing on one solution, and difficulties in discussing and negotiating with regulatory bodies, led him eventually into trouble with the US authorities. Tragically, he died in prison in 1957.

His therapeutic work was continued by his students, in particular Alexander Lowen. Lowen developed Bioenergetic Analysis - a diagnostic and treatment method - based on Reich's Character Analysis. Lowen worked with clients one to one for many decades. He would analyse their body posture and listen to details of what happened in their childhoods and, from that, work out their character type. This done, he would get them to perform certain Bioenergetics postures or to express emotions. The treatment would often last several years, but he had major successes and wrote many books from all the insights he garnered.

In addition, he created the International Institute for Bioenergetic Analysis (IIBA). This organisation holds trainings and licenses therapists worldwide.

Although successful in practice, Bioenergetics emerged at a time when more mind-based therapies were coming to the fore in mainstream psychology. Cognitive-behavioural therapy (CBT), for example, focussed on the relationship between thinking and behaviour. It proved so popular and successful that, for a whole generation of therapists, it seemed that the mind and thinking would provide all the answers. Bioenergetics and other body-based therapies found themselves swept out of fashion, consigned to the periphery.

In the 1970s, as the "flower power" revolution took hold, however, many novel therapies involving sexuality and the body developed an underground following, attracting people from way outside the mainstream.

Most prominent in this field was the Indian guru, the Bhagwan Shree Rajneesh, known today as Osho. Osho insisted that, for Westerners to be able to experience meditation, they would first need to participate in a lot of cathartic release, as their minds were over-burdened with worries and the past. He also had a strong disdain for mind-based therapy and, as a former philosophy professor, could put his arguments out convincingly. Osho created "active meditations" to support followers to release the past. Most famous of these was Osho Dynamic Meditation, which included elements of Bioenergetics and Emotional Expression.

Osho's teaching and meditations aside, the atmosphere he created around him in his ashrams in India and the US served as a "melting pot" for therapists and therapy. Hundreds of therapists from all over the States and Europe travelled there, along with thousands of young spiritual seekers. In this vibrant field of exploration and experimentation, knowledge about Bioenergetics and other body-based therapies expanded considerably.

In 2020, the reality is that Bioenergetics struggles to survive. Technological advances have led our culture to being more and more mind-based. As this happens, it's become easier and easier for us to leave our body behind. Over the years that I have been in the scene, I have witnessed many people who stumbled across Bioenergetics and who were amazed at how much it could transform them. They were incredulous that it hadn't caught on more. But this is how it is.

Currently, Bioenergetics is flourishing most in Latin America and southern Europe, especially Brazil, Italy, Spain and Portugal. In these countries the need for bodily movement is better recognised as a prerequisite for health. On the east and west coasts of the USA it has also retained a healthy presence.

There is remarkably little practical, written information about Bioenergetics in the English language. This was the principal motivation for me to write this book. I consider that it would be a tragedy if knowledge of this transformative therapy disappeared from our culture.

How to Do Bioenergetics

In essence, practising Bioenergetic is remarkably simple. You put your body into certain postures, you breathe, usually through the mouth, and you feel your body. The majority of Bioenergetic postures, especially those used to treat repression, follow this simple formula.

- Maintain posture
- Breathe through the mouth
- Feel your body

So, for example, if you were going to try the Arch posture, #4.1 in this book, you would simply do the following:

- Stand upright
- Lean forwards until you are in the Arch pose, as shown in the diagram
- Check that you have certain elements of the body posture correct
- Breathe through the mouth deeply
- Feel your body
- Remain in the posture, breathing and feeling, until the allotted time is up

That is really all there is to it. However, it's important to be aware of a few things which tend to slip people up.

Firstly, because of the way our minds work, people tend to overfocus on the posture and the length of time they can hold it for. But, in so doing, they neglect to breathe deeply and to really feel their body. This actually achieves very little. It's important to recognise that the posture, while important, is only one of three vital elements. You must also be breathing deeply and staying in touch with your body. When you can do all three of these together the release will happen naturally and spontaneously.

Related to this, be careful not to obsess over how long you can hold the posture for. It's great to work up the length of time that you can stay in a pose. But if you achieve this by holding your body tight, clinging on desperately and praying for the bell to ring, then once again you won't really have achieved so much. You have to remain deeply breathing and feeling to get the best results.

Finally, as we shall see, there is a phenomenon called Resistance, which invariably soon comes into play. I will discuss that more, later in this chapter.

The Edge of the Comfort Zone

The edge of your comfort zone is where change happens naturally. This concept is very important in Bioenergetics, and many other areas of life too.

Doing Bioenergetics, you will constantly be dealing with discomfort. The postures we work with put your body under controlled, intelligent stress and it will, at times, be uncomfortable. This is part of it. It's important that you know how to be with this discomfort.

The basic strategy is as follows:

- As the position gets uncomfortable, increase the depth of your breathing to see if you can breathe through the discomfort.
- If you can, great. Then continue until you come to a deeper level of discomfort.
- If you can't breathe through the discomfort, then simply accept that you are now at the edge of your comfort zone and come out of the posture.

You won't achieve much if you are always comfortable. But, likewise, you won't achieve much if you're always pushing yourself into pain. The edge of the comfort zone is the place where natural, spontaneous change happens, outside the realm of mental control.

The reason that it's important to try to breathe through discomfort is because of how we've learned to deal with physical and emotional stress in the past. The basic strategy most humans employ, when discomfort comes, is to clench at the throat. But this merely locks the stress in and allows us to try and manage it. It doesn't facilitate a release. Therefore, it's really important to do your best to increase your breathing as discomfort comes in a posture. You may find that a deep release starts to take place.

How Bioenergetics Works

The postures found in Bioenergetics put different muscles, or muscle groups, under a degree of controlled, intelligent stress. In this stressed state, they can actually start to release holding patterns and dead zones from the past. Breathing deeply at the same time increases the level of vital energy in your system, thereby supporting this release to go deeper.

A good analogy is an old dishcloth. You may recall finding an old cloth under the sink, all dried up and not much use for anything. This old cloth is in a state analogous to a muscle that is riddled with holding patterns. It has no resilience - because it has no flexibility. But, if we pour water on the cloth and start to wring it out, slowly its resilience returns. With our muscles, it's not that we pour liquid on them. But this is a good analogy for what happens when we increase our breathing, and really feel into our muscles.

It may seem strange that, in order to relax more deeply, we first need to put ourselves under more stress. But this is the reality of how Bioenergetics works. When you breathe through the slowly rising discomfort, you may even find your muscles start to shake or vibrate spontaneously. Truth is, they can't wait to get the holding out!

Breathing through the Mouth

Breathing through the mouth is a vital element of Bioenergetics. It more deeply oxygenates your body and so increases the level of vibrant energy inside. It is this vital, active energy that we are utilising to drive out the old, stuck charge from the past that our muscles are carrying. So, I do highly recommend that you breathe deeply through the mouth while following the exercises. If however, you find this makes you feel dizzy, feel free to either reduce your breathing level or go to nasal breathing instead.

Resistance & The Defensive Layer

Now, let us consider this vital topic. Without an understanding of resistance, it will be truly hard to make progress in Bioenergetics when working by yourself.

Resistance is the struggle we experience to do something that we know is good for us. It's the unwillingness to go through a little discomfort for the greater good. Our mind gets used to negotiating its way through the day without bringing us into too deep a confrontation with the charge inside. We supplement this with our habits, rituals, routines and the daily substances we like to take. Yes, of course, we say we want to change. But showing up for change on a regular basis is not easy, as many of us have discovered.

Underneath those thoughts that we "can't be bothered" doing something today, or that we'll do it "later," is the work of the brain's defensive layer. Earlier we saw how traumatic events triggered a response in the brain that offset feeling. Likewise, when old, stored feelings are brought out of the muscle system back towards awareness, this response comes into action again.

In order to process the past, we have to be open to feel. The feelings held inside may be far less intense than we imagine them to be, but we need to be open to them regardless. But, as old feelings start to rise into our awareness, for processing, our defensive layer may well kick in and try to get us out of there - before that can happen.

We may sense a vague anxiety and cease our Bioenergetic exercise. Or we may "suddenly remember" something else we need to do and just stop. The defensive layer knows how to get us out of there. It's like the famous, loyal Japanese soldier, still fighting the war three decades after it's over, refusing to stand down.

This is the reason why deep therapeutic progress is so hard to accomplish alone. Because, at the time we most need to stay with something, most of us will succumb to our mind's avoidance strategies. For this reason, Bioenergetics has in the past only been practised one to one with a therapist. Or in a group, again with someone skilled running the session.

If you want to have any chance of making progress alone, you will need to be willing to take on your personal defensive layer. This means, having a basic level of discipline when you set up a session for yourself. You will need to plan it out and commit to completing it. While practising, you will need to check that you are breathing deep and remaining present. Most of all, you will need to ensure that, when your mind is coming up with reasons why you should stop early, instead of doing that, you use this as a signpost that you need to go deeper.

If you can do this - if you can learn to work constructively with your own resistance, and use it as a signpost for when to really focus, then you can create immense change working on your own.

How Does it Feel when we do Bioenergetics?

One question that I often get asked about Bioenergetics is this. As we open up the muscles of the body, do we need to re-experience all the old feelings that we've been repressing? The answer is generally no. Some people do find old, lost memories coming to the surface. They may recall times in their childhood that they would rather not. They may find themselves briefly overwhelmed by feelings. But the majority relate that they simply experience more openness, more positivity and a deeper sense of being grounded as they continue with this practice. On occasions, often in the early stages, we may find ourselves more emotionally volatile, more prone to anger or vulnerability. But this soon stabilises.

However, this said, it is important that you are open to feel. If you have a strong "no" to the feelings held inside, this will not support you to grow. So, while it's not usually the case that you need to feel all that is repressed inside of you, you do need to be open to feeling in order for Bioenergetics to work.

It's normal for people to find Bioenergetics quite a struggle to begin with. I'm not going to sugar coat it for you. You will likely hate it, and this is a normal human reaction. But, hopefully, with each session that you complete, you begin to notice positive changes in how open and how grounded you feel, and how you relate to others. Hopefully, your mind will see that the rewards outweigh the benefits and you will persevere, continuing to become the most beautiful and powerful being you can be. That is my wish.

Grounding

Thus far we've looked fairly extensively at how Bioenergetics works to remove the charge from our muscle system, that which has accumulated from trauma and conditioning. However, there are other ways that Bioenergetics works to free us from the past. We will now look at some of these, starting with "Grounding."

Most people, on an inner level, spend their days managing all the feelings that they have pent up inside of them. This is all done in the upper body. It's like their whole body, from the solar plexus up, is a sealed container and all that can be done with all the anxious energy inside, is to just keep it moving around so that it doesn't become overwhelming. But this is not how it is supposed to be.

The lower half of our body - our belly, pelvis, legs, ankles and feet - should connect us to the earth and allow excess energy to flow away naturally. When the muscles of these areas are open, you actually feel a constant flow of energy in your lower body. You feel like you're connected to the earth. But all these muscle groups become riddled with holding and dead zones too. And so we become cut off from the earth.

Therefore, grounding ourselves is another key principle and core function of Bioenergetics. All it involves is getting all the lower body muscles more and more open, so that we no longer have to manage our anxiety, but can simply allow it to flow away to earth.

Once you get to the exercises in this book, you will notice that, the first chapter aside, we start with the feet and work up. This is to support the grounding process, thus increasing the release!

The "Mental Compensation" Principle

One useful way of envisioning the body is as a team. Neural capacity is not exclusive to our frontal lobes and prefrontal cortex, the areas where our "thinking intelligence," or "mind," dominate. Many, older areas of our brain have intelligence, as do areas of our body. Our belly, in particular, has its own neural circuitry, the enteric nervous system (ENS).

In a healthy individual, all these areas of the body function as a team. The team may have a leader, the prefrontal cortex, but everyone is included. However, because most of us have progressively evacuated the body, to dwell mostly in the thinking mind, so many elements of this team have become cut off.

Our body has become like a badly functioning company, perhaps similar to the one in the popular UK and US television series, The Office. The CEO is behaving like a petty dictator and team members have become uninspired and dysfunctional.

When one element of our body's team has become cut off, the thinking mind will endeavour to take on its role. Over time, this can have extreme consequences.

For example, our spine not only keeps us upright but also keeps us feeling like we have the right to take a position for ourselves. When we lose awareness of our spine, our mind will attempt to maintain this feeling of our right to individuality. But it will do so by creating a lot of tension, especially in our neck and shoulder area.

Our belly serves the psychological function of maintaining healthy boundaries. If we become cut off from the feeling of our belly, once again our mind will attempt to take on this role. Its way, again, is the way of extreme control. It will keep on the alert for any sense of invasion, physical or psychological, and again tense our upper body every time it senses danger.

Over time, if we remain cut off from our belly or our spine, our mind will simply create more and more stress and tension in our lives, especially in our upper body. People suffering in this way may try to get their back and shoulders more relaxed, perhaps through massage, meditation or yoga. But, as we can see, this is really just putting a band-aid over the issue. Once we have more awareness of our spine and our belly, our mind can relax. It no longer needs to try and take on these roles. Our upper body will relax, and stay relaxed.

Thus, another aspect of Bioenergetics is to bring more awareness back into these key areas. In this book, you will find many exercises working with these areas of the body, as well as others where the same principle applies.

Opening Somatic Centres

Many of our human emotions appear to be sourced from specific areas of our body. Anger seems rooted in the belly. Love and emotional pain seem to arise from the heart (the heart centre in the middle of our chest). Expression itself seems to be regulated at the throat.

The belief in our mind that we need to strongly control our feelings in order to get social needs met results in us contracting around these somatic centres. For example, we may develop a lot of tension around the throat and neck. We might learn to tense our belly or we might bloat it out with unhealthy foods. Some people learn to keep the muscles between the shoulder blades tight, so that their hearts can't open.

So, some of the Bioenergetic exercises in this book will work to slowly re-open these centres, allowing us to feel and release our pain, to hold safe boundaries by feeling clear with anger, and to reaffirm our right to express ourselves, however we might be.

Primal Movements or Gestures

Another principle that Bioenergetics makes use of relates to primal movements or gestures. Our body is a treasure house of instinctual reflexes and responses, some stretching back deep into our evolutionary past. Re-activating these old circuits in the body can help us to release unnatural tensions, to feel more animal vitality and to create a sense of embodied awareness within us. So, watch out for these kinds of exercises too!

A Few Common Questions

I will close this chapter by answering a couple of common questions that people have about the theory of Bioenergetics.

Question: Can you map out an exact relationship between areas of our body and areas of our psychology?

Answer: There is some degree of broad correlation, but we are not simple machines, rather very complex and highly networked processors. Thus, it is valid to say that if you get more awareness of your belly, you will feel more empowered. Also, that if you remove any holding around your throat, you will find it easier to speak your truth. But it would not be especially valid to say that anger is held in the masseter muscles of the face, as was commonly believed back in the 50s.

In addition, be aware that mobilising the stuck energy (charge) in one area of your body may not create a complete release. It may simply become held in another area. This is why we work all around the body.

Question: What I've suffered in the past seems so extreme, I don't think I can ever be healed from it.

Answer: While you need to be open to experiencing feelings, be aware that all you really need to heal is to release the energy bound in the muscles. That binding happened during the trauma. Once that holding is out, you will feel far more free from the past. You don't by any means need to re-experience exactly what took place. Though, as mentioned, you do need to be open to feel whatever does come up.

How to Practise?

Okay, so now that you've heard all about how much positive change Bioenergetics can create, it's time to get down to the exercises themselves.

For this book, I'm basically assuming that you will be working largely on your own or perhaps with a friend or partner, but not with someone experienced or qualified in this field.

This is fully do-able and, with willpower, you will be able to create a lot of positive change. But I would also like to mention that it will be invaluable if you can at times come along for a group or a one-to-one session with someone who is experienced. Not only might you learn more exercises but you will also get feedback on how you can improve the postures you already know. This can be incredibly useful as it is so easy to slip into bad habits and then you don't get the change you deserve.

Creating a Schedule

Something that supports most people massively with Bioenergetics is to create a daily or weekly schedule. Actually write something down, or create a chart that you can tick off when complete. It can be very satisfying to fill those boxes in! Before you do this, look practically at how much time you can commit. Maybe you can actually only do one 30-minute session a week. That is okay. Just create a schedule for that.

I would say, for beginners, that if you can commit to 20 minutes a day, 5 days a week, then this is perfect.

The Best Time of Day to do Bioenergetics

I recommend the early morning, ideally right after getting out of bed, and before drinking coffee or tea. This is because, when we awaken, all our unconscious, half-processed issues are right there, close to the surface. This is the ideal time to create change. However, if you need a coffee first, or you can't fit it in until later in the day, then that is absolutely fine. In fact, whenever you can consistently fit a Bioenergetics practice in will work well.

Some people are fine to do Bioenergetics late at night, before sleeping. They find that it doesn't disturb their sleep. However, for many people, this will not work. The exercises can energise you a lot and so, for most, it is not useful to do Bioenergetics late at night. If you are interested in doing something later in the day then please check out Chapter 16, where there are some great suggestions for this.

Developing Will Power

In my experience as a therapist, the main issue most beginners experience is developing the willpower or discipline to keep going even when their mind doesn't want to. We live in a comfort-driven world and it is not easy to hold to a path that at times will inevitably be uncomfortable. Many give up right when change is just around the corner.

As we saw in Chapter 2, we will resist change, simply because we prefer to cling to what we know, however unsatisfactory. If you are going to work successfully on your own, you will need to be able to evaluate rationally any reasons you give yourself for giving up and check out if they're real. You will need to develop a basic level of discipline.

The best way I know to increase your discipline is by creating accountability. Look around for a friend, perhaps someone who also wants to get into this practice, though that needn't be the case. Ask them to support you by checking in with you daily if you've completed your Bioenergetics session. Knowing someone is there to hold you accountable is a phenomenally powerful support.

The best way to make use of this is to commit in advance to a certain number of days, perhaps thirty, and for a length of time each day. Decide in advance if you're going to have weekends off or not. Set it up so that you can't wriggle out. You know best how tricky you can be, so make sure you create a structure that you can't easily back out of.

If you know that your willpower is weak then you can also try including belly and backbone exercises - like Bear Crawl and Belly Activation - in your daily routine from the beginning. As you become more aware of your belly and your backbone you will find it easier to hold to a path that will at times be uncomfortable.

The Right Attitude when Practising

While practising Bioenergetics try to have a meditative attitude. As much as you can, stay focussed on the feeling of your body, while breathing through the mouth. Try not to be judgmental about how it feels. Try not to get involved in analysis. Simply keep breathing. Keep being present in your body, and keep accepting. This is the ideal. And, of course, because we are human and this is an intense and confrontational practice, at times it will be hard to simply accept. But do what you can and continue regardless.

I learned, after some years of my journey with Bioenergetics, that it didn't really matter what I thought about it. Some days I was really present, sometimes it was really a struggle. Some days I couldn't wait to start, some I would procrastinate and make constant excuses to myself. But I learned that if I did it then my day would be better, and with that, my life would be better. I learned to largely disregard what my mind thought about it on any given day, a humbling experience.

As well as being meditative, also be thorough. While in a posture, really check the points of the posture that are listed in this book. Are your feet placed correctly? Are you breathing properly? Are your shoulders as they should be? Are your eyes open? Go through and check. Don't just assume that you've got it right. The more thorough you can be, the more you will internalize the principles, and the more you will release.

Many of the exercises will be uncomfortable. Even if they're not uncomfortable to start with, they will soon become so as you remain in the posture! This is a big part of Bioenergetics. It is uncomfortable and learning to deal with discomfort meditatively is a huge part of the practice.

When discomfort comes try to breathe through it. That means increasing the depth of your breath through the mouth, in and out. What we learned as kids was to contract at the throat when physical or psychological stress was happening. This is not healthy and only locks old feelings within. So, make use of the experience of discomfort to really practice opening your throat and breathing deep.

When the discomfort gets too much to breathe through, then you know that this is your limit. It's the length of time to set on your timer. I will give average lengths of time to hold a pose for most exercises as we go along. But be aware that this is just an average and that it is best to see how long works for your body. As you continue along your journey with Bioenergetics, you can progressively increase the length of time you hold the posture, or increase the number of repetitions. Please make sure you are familiar with the section in Chapter 2 entitled, "The Edge of the Comfort Zone."

Which Exercises Should I Start With?

If you've already flicked through this book, and seen the wealth of exercises contained within, you may be thinking something along the lines of… Where on earth do I start?! Should I do the exercises that most appeal to me? Or maybe the ones I'm avoiding? Or the ones that correspond to where I feel I have issues?

To help you here, I have included in Chapter 17 twelve weeks of exercises that will be suitable for most people. If you would like to follow a longer course, in a structured way, then please check out the Bioenergetics Online Training Academy at https://bioenergetics.org.uk.

Equipment You Will Need

You really don't need to make much investment to get into Bioenergetics. You don't need any expensive equipment, the best workout clothes, or a perfect studio in which to practice. In fact, it can be better to just make use of what you have to hand, and not seek out anything special. This can help you to focus your mind internally, a key element of Bioenergetics.

You can practice Bioenergetics perfectly well in a 10-foot square space (3 metres square) and with only an absolute minimum outlay.

Here is a list of what you will need if you're to complete most of the exercises in this book:

- a human body, ideally with a good bit of trauma and conditioning.
- loose clothing - T-shirt, tracksuit bottoms, this kind of thing.
- a dinging app on your phone, or ding tracks that you've downloaded. Most of the exercises are timed and it's important that you don't have to look at a clock or watch to know when to change. Ding track mp3s of different lengths can be downloaded from my website - see the Resources chapter at the end of the book. When playing them ensure you set your music player to constantly repeat the same track.
- a yoga mat or two. These I don't use for many exercises, but a good solid one (when rolled up) makes a great bolster for some of the floor exercises.
- a foam roller. These are normally used to roll out muscles after a workout. There are a couple of Bioenergetics postures that make use of a foam roller, so you may wish to purchase one.

- a Bioenergetic Stool. A stalwart piece of kit for Bioenergetics in the old days. These days I usually recommend that people make use of a fairly solid sofa. But if you'd like to make one, see the Resources chapter at the end of the book for details.
- a spit bucket. A washing-up bowl with tissue in it works fine. For the belly exercises in particular, you may feel nausea. It can be very healing to spit.

In Chapter 14, there are a few Bioenergetic exercises that incorporate elements of Emotional Expression. These will need a few extra bits and bobs, which are listed there.

People for whom Bioenergetics May Not Be Suitable

There are people for whom Bioenergetics may not be suitable, or who may need to seek expert advice before starting. As a therapy, Bioenergetics works directly with the bodily manifestation of trauma and conditioning. It does not work via the thinking mind.

As such, you do need to have a relatively normal ego to practice Bioenergetics without expert supervision. In practical terms, this means that if you have a history of severe psychiatric issues then Bioenergetics may not be what you need. Persons who have been diagnosed with the following conditions would usually be excluded from working alone:

- a history of psychotic episodes
- schizophrenia
- bi-polar disorder

- related conditions usually treated with heavy, suppressive medications

For persons in these categories, you will need expert supervision if you are to try Bioenergetics. If too much repressed emotion or trauma is unlocked at one time, you may find yourself triggered back into old defensive strategies before you can really recognise what is happening. You may not have had a psychotic episode or an incidence of bi-polar for a decade, but you could find yourself back there, and obviously, this is not beneficial.

People Suffering Depression or Anxiety

People with more "low-level" mental health conditions may find Bioenergetics useful. But it is important, especially if you are on medication, to check in with a suitably qualified person before trying the exercises in this book.

If you already see a psychotherapist or a counsellor, let them know, so that you can discuss anything that arises from your work with this practice. Remember, Bioenergetics was originally undertaken in tandem with regular psychotherapy. While it is not necessary to have psychotherapy if you're doing Bioenergetics, the combination of the two is a very powerful tool for transformation.

Here is a list of people who will need to get medical advice prior to trying Bioenergetics:

- people who have been, at any time, diagnosed with a psychiatric condition.
- people taking any form of inhibitory or mood-altering medication.

- people with a history of injecting drug use.
- people with an injury or operation to one of the body areas used in a specific Bioenergetic exercise.
- people who are pregnant.

People with Some Form of Physical Limitation

If you have an injury, or other issue, in an area of your body used in a specific Bioenergetic exercise, then please ensure you check in with a suitably qualified person before attempting that exercise.

Format for Exercises in this Book

Individual chapters, from now on, will cover different areas of the body and different types of exercises. To aid understanding, each exercise will be described in a similar way. This will include:

- Name of exercise - and numeration for reference.
- Introduction, including psychological significance of the exercise.
- Equipment needed, if any.
- Environment, where something specific is needed.
- Background music, where useful.
- Timing and Repetitions.
- Warm-up, Rest Position & Closing.
- Method - How to do it, in words and pictures, including points of the posture to note and check.
- Significant variations.

If one of these headings isn't present for a specific exercise, this simply means it does not apply to that exercise.

A Few Final Questions

Here are a few common questions that people have about the actual practice of Bioenergetics, together with answers.

Question: Are there elements of posture which are common to all Bioenergetic exercises?

Answer: Yes. When in a standing posture, you will invariably need to have your knees slightly bent and not locked straight. Locked knees prevent a good energy flow up and down the body. In addition, nearly all Bioenergetic exercises require you to breathe through the mouth, to bring more energy, charge and feeling into the trunk of your body.

Question: I've been practising an exercise for a while now and want to go deeper with it. Should I do it for a longer period of time, or increase the number of repetitions?

Answer: Generally, I find that increasing the number of reps creates a deeper release. This is because the body learns with each rep how to release more. However, it is also good to experiment with holding certain postures for longer time frames too. This is especially true with the Bow & Arch posture (Chapter 4).

Question: When I do certain postures, I find my body, or a part of it, starts to shake spontaneously. Or, I see other people shaking when doing Bioenergetics but I don't. Am I not doing it right?

Answer: Spontaneous shaking is common when doing Bioenergetics but there are no hard principles about why it happens or what value it has. For some people, this shaking is clearly a sign of a deep release spontaneously taking place from the muscles. For others, it may simply be a sign of vibrant aliveness. For others still, it may actually be a sign of avoidance. Their body shakes off the surface tension as a strategy to avoid confrontation with the more deeply structured complex that lies beneath. So, if you shake, great. If you don't, please don't be too concerned about this.

The Bow & Arch

The Bow & Arch is a cornerstone of Bioenergetics practice. For this reason, I'm devoting a whole chapter to it. After this, we will work through the body from the feet up.

These two postures, the Bow and the Arch, form a truly powerful and transformative practice. If your only knowledge of Bioenergetics was the Bow & Arch, and you practised it daily, you would find yourself considerably transformed over time. This is because it slowly re-leases the charge from key areas of our muscle system.

One thing that many people find confusing about the Bow & Arch is the way that different names have arisen over time for the two postures. Some practitioners call the Bow - the Arch! Some call the Arch, the Ground-reach, or Forward Bend. Other variations exist. It's all good. There is no single, worldwide organisation that controls Bioenergetics so these things are somewhat inevitable.

In like manner, there are several variations on how to actually practise these two exercises. I will cover the main variations in this chapter.

This pair of postures, usually practised one after the other, and repeated three times around, open up key areas of our body - the lower back and the backs of the legs. These are the areas most used by our brain to store the charge from repressed feelings. When practised a certain way, the Bow exercise also opens up the shoulders and the area between the shoulder blades, another area of huge holding.

The Bow & Arch is an excellent long-term treatment for anxiety. In the context of Body-based Therapy, anxiety is created by the charge of energy bound into the muscles through repression. This charge exerts a pull on the psyche and when it's triggered, it creates the belief in the mind that we are "not okay as we are." From this belief, we seek to change how we feel. We drink coffee, eat sugary snacks, scroll online, anything that changes our underlying state. But, because of our constant avoidance, the underlying feeling in the body never gets to be processed. People thus remain prone to anxiety their whole lives.

The Bow & Arch will slowly and progressively remove this charge leaving us feeling more and more secure in our bodies. It's great to do, whether you are feeling anxious or not.

Let's take a look at the exercises themselves.

Timing & Repetitions: With this Bioenergetic exercise, in particular, different people do need to start with different lengths of time to hold each pose. There's no universal rule. What I recommend is that you first go into the Arch pose, with a watch beside you, and see how long you can stay there until it gets too uncomfortable. When discomfort first comes, do try to breathe through it. When it's too much, come out of the posture and record how long you stayed in the pose. Now repeat this with the Bow, once again recording how long you could stay in the pose before it became too uncomfortable. Whichever of these times is the shortest, set your dinging device to that length of time for the Bow & Arch. Feel free to increase it after a few days or weeks. With the Bow & Arch, 3 repetitions are standard. Just to be clear, there should be no break between these reps.

Warm Up, Rest Position & Closing: You don't need to be warmed up before beginning. Neither does this exercise require a Rest Position between reps. To close, simply give yourself at least 5 to 10 minutes down-time after completing the 3 reps. You can sit or lie down and relax, trying to remain feeling your body the whole time.

4.1 The Arch

Method:
- Set your dinger for the correct length of time for you - see above.
- Stand upright, facing straight ahead, with your feet about 30cm apart, and the outsides of your feet roughly parallel. Have your eyes open and keep them that way throughout the Bow & Arch. Breathe fairly deeply and slowly through your mouth, in and out.
- Now, allow your head to drop slowly. When your chin reaches your chest - or has got as close as it can, hang slowly forwards until your fingertips are either just off the floor

or you are as low as you can go - see illustration. If you are quite flexible and can easily touch the floor in this pose then bring yourself back up a little so that your fingertips are off the floor.

☛ Check these elements of your posture:

☞ Check that your neck and shoulders are loose. Do this by giving your head and your arms a little jiggle or swirl around to prove to yourself they are loose. They should be hanging like those of a rag doll. When we are used to controlling our feelings unnaturally, the head will tend to pull up, away from the body and the arms will pull towards the legs. We don't want this to happen.

☞ Check that your weight is slightly forwards, more towards your toes than your heels. But keep your heels on the floor.

☞ Pull your tailbone upward, creating a counter-stretch in your legs, but keeping a little flexibility in the knees. Your legs should be nearly straight but with a tiny bit of flex left in the knees.

☞ Check that your eyes are open and that you are breathing nice and deep through the mouth, in and out. Also check that your awareness is on your body, feeling what's happening.

☛ When the ding comes, move directly into the Bow posture as guided below.

4.2 The Bow

Method:

☛ Come up slowly from the Arch position, feeling your body as you move. Your head comes up last.

☛ Once standing, begin to bring your arms straight up above your head, palms facing forwards and roughly parallel, and then stretch them back behind the ears. At the same time, push your pelvis forwards and stick your chest out - see illustration. The knees should remain slightly bent. Make your body into the shape of an archer's bow, but with your head remaining upright, eyes open, looking straight ahead. Hold this position until the ding, breathing deeply throughout.

☛ When the ding comes, go down once more into the Arch pose. Perform 3 reps and then sit or lie down and rest for 5 to 10 minutes. Remain feeling your body.

Now I will list and explain some variations. None require any equipment. Timing, reps, Rest Positions and Closing are all the same as for the Bow & Arch above, so I won't list them for each variation.

4.3 Standing Bow

Method:

☛ Stand upright with your arms outstretched above your head, as in the regular Bow, but with your fingers fully splayed. Like the regular Bow, your feet should be about 30cm apart.

☛ In the regular Bow (4.2) you would push your pelvis forwards. But in this version you keep your legs straight and lean back from the hips as far as you can. As in the regular Bow, stretch your arms back as far as possible, but in this version allow your neck to also follow, so that you are gazing slightly upwards. Maintain this position for one ding.

☛ When the ding sounds, hang forwards into the regular Arch pose for the same length of time. Repeat 3 times.

4.4 The Bow (Lowen Version)

This version of the posture is favoured by therapists from Alexander Lowen's school, the IIBA. It will be found clearly described in his book, "Bioenergetics." It may be particularly useful if you find version 4.2 is creating pain in your mid-back. Or if you know your back is especially "bendy."

Method:

- ☞ This posture has two variations from 4.2, above - one obvious and one more subtle.
- ☞ Firstly, instead of putting your arms up above your head, you make gentle fists and place them in the small of your lower back. It's as though you were using your arms to push your lower back forwards.
- ☞ Secondly, and more subtly, instead of pushing your pelvis fully forwards, you bend your knees slightly more and keep your pelvis a little back, as though you were more "sitting down" on it. You press your lower back forwards instead.
- ☞ This variation can be done with Arch (4.1) as a counter-stretch if desired.

4.5 Vibrating Arch

This variation of the regular Arch posture (4.1) can support a spontaneous shaking release from the legs.

Method:

☛ Hang forwards in the Arch pose, 4.1, checking the usual elements of the posture.

☛ Now, gently bring your hands to the floor in front of you, taking roughly half of your weight. The best is to rest on the area between your 1st and 2nd set of knuckles, counting from the wrist. This helps stop your wrists from locking, which can happen if you put your palms flat down. Keep your neck loose, head just hanging.

☛ Gently lift your ass, while straightening your legs, and see if a natural vibration comes into your legs. If so, allow this. If not, don't worry. You can adjust the distance between your hands and your feet if desired, to see if this encourages spontaneous shaking to occur.

☛ When the ding comes, gently come up into the regular Bow posture for the same length of time. Repeat 3 times.

4.6 Bow with Heels Raised

This is a variation specifically for those who find staying in the regular Bow posture difficult. Sometimes this is due to excess tension in the mid back.

Equipment: You will need a phone directory or something similarly shaped of similar height and width. It should have a thickness of around an inch (2.5cm).

Method:

- ☛ Take a phone directory or similar sized book and place it on the floor.
- ☛ Stand with your toes on the floor and your heels resting upon the book.
- ☛ Lean back into the regular Bow posture, 4.2.
- ☛ At the ding, hang forwards into the regular Arch posture, but with your heels now on the floor, and repeat 3 times.

Note: Experiment with the thickness of the book until you find what works for you. Over time, you may find that your body posture changes and you no longer need to rest on the book.

4.7 One-Legged Arch

Method:

- ☛ Lean forwards into the regular Arch pose.
- ☛ Drop both palms to the floor, supporting your weight roughly evenly between your hands and feet.

- ☛ Keeping your left leg firm, lift your right leg behind you, stretching up as far as you can.
- ☛ At the ding, come up into the regular Bow pose.
- ☛ At the next ding, return to the Arch pose with palms down, and this time lift the left leg.
- ☛ Return to the Bow posture at the ding. Repeat 3 times. For the final Arch, you can keep both feet and palms on the floor.

4.8 Bow & Arch with Expression

Just as we can make slight alterations to the postures, to see if our body releases more, or slightly differently, so we can also add an element of expression to the Bow & Arch. The Arch position does not lend itself to release, as we are leant forwards with our throat somewhat closed. But the Bow position is good for release. You need to ensure that you are practising in an environment where you can make noise without disturbing others.

Here are some different ways you can add an element of expression while in the Bow posture:

- Laughing: Laughing is an excellent form of emotional release. In the Bow posture, simply start laughing, ideally quite loudly and from the belly. A classic, Santa Claus "Ho, ho, ho" style laugh is the best. You will likely feel any sense of stiffness in the posture shift.
- Gargoyle Release: Open your eyes wide, your mouth wide, stick your tongue out and make a hissing sound.
- Positivity: Stretched into the Bow posture, with your arms up as high as you can, shout out "I can do it!" and free associate with positive suggestions. This can be very powerful and really shift your energy. Other positive sentences you can use include:
  - ☞ I can have the life I want
  - ☞ I can have the friends I want
  - ☞ I can have the lovers I want

☞ I can have the job I want
☞ I have the right
☞ I have the power

When adding elements of expression to the Bow posture, try to do it in a structured rather than random way. This means deciding in advance what you're going to do and for roughly how long.

Rest Positions

Before we start working our way through the body, it will be helpful to go through the variety of "Rest Positions" that are made use of, either between postures, or to close an exercise with.

When closing an exercise, there are two basic approaches. Either you go straight into relaxation and integration, as in just sitting or lying down on the floor. Or you add a stage where some gentle, spontaneous release can occur, and then go into relaxation.

For the latter, you might choose the Shaking posture, 5.4. Or the final Psoas Release posture, 8.7, posture 3.

Adding this stage is useful because the body frequently likes to release more once the exercise you've been doing is complete. If you put a gentle release exercise in, like those suggested above, you may find that your body starts to shake spontaneously for a while, and this is great. After this, you can go into relaxation. Give it a try.

How you close the posture or workout is actually very important. A lot of processing happens during the closing, even if we're not aware of it. So don't be too keen to just get on with your day. Make sure you allocate adequate time, in advance, to close and to integrate.

Our culture tends to predispose us, with Bioenergetics, to focus strongly on the posture and downplay the role of breathing, feeling and closing. But breathing and feeling are in fact equally, if not more, important. All the closing postures in this book require you to continue to focus on the sensation of the body - because it is actually this that finally creates the healing.

Now let's look at some Rest Positions. With these postures you don't need any equipment, timing or repetitions.

5.1 Classic Leg Rest

I make use of this simple, lying down pose frequently.

Method:
☛ Lie flat on your back with the back of your head resting on the floor and your arms relaxed by your sides, with palms facing up. Have the soles of your feet flat on the floor with your knees up.

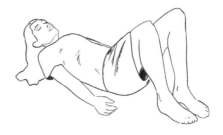

5.2 Diamond Leg Posture (Supta bada Konasana)

This posture is a great way to integrate after opening up the back and, indeed, can be practised in its own right. It may be done with your lower back flat on the floor, or with a bolster under it.

Method:

- Lie on your back and bring the soles of your feet together, with your heels close to your ass.
- Allow your knees to fall to the side naturally, not forcing them down.
- Close your eyes, breathe gently through the mouth and feel your body.

5.3 Lying Down Rest Pose

This is a posture for total, lying down relaxation.

Method:

- Lie flat on the floor with your legs outstretched and your arms relaxed by your side, palms facing up. Ensure that the back of your head rests on the floor and that your neck is relaxed. Your eyes are closed.

5.4 Shaking Posture

Shaking the body is a great way to allow integration after a posture while also keeping your energy moving. And there is a "right way" to shake in Bioenergetics!

Method:

☛ Stand upright with your feet roughly shoulder-width apart. Breathe through the mouth quite deeply in and out and feel into your legs. Look for any sensation of trembling or shakiness. If you find it, then allow it to propagate up your body, creating a vertical shake. If there's no feeling of shakiness in the legs, this is fine. Simply begin to gently shake your body up and down.

☛ While shaking, continue to breathe deeply in and out through the mouth and continue to put your attention on your body. The practice will usually feel quite intense if you are really staying present. It's important to try and relax your neck so that your head can just bob up and down like it's just another part of your body.

☛ Note: Do not shake your body from side to side. This type of gentle release through shaking requires a vertical shake with the neck loose. This method of shaking resembles that which animals use instinctively when releasing shock from their system (see Polyvagal theory if interested). Side to side shaking is occasionally used for a different type of release.

☛ You may well have to "fake it until you make it" and this is fine. If you would like to see people shaking correctly in this manner, perhaps look online for videos of people doing the first stage of Osho Kundalini Meditation. Osho was a great proponent of shaking. Incidentally, shaking the body was also a cornerstone practice of the Subud religion of Indonesia, who called it "latihan." Followers would shake for hours at a time as a practice in its own right. You can also look up Ratu Bagus, a "shaking guru" in Bali, if you're interested.

5.5 Child Pose

I make use of this great, integrating posture in several of the exercises in this book. It is also found in many Yoga traditions.

Method:

☞ Kneel down on the floor. You should have your feet close together, perhaps with big toes gently touching. Your knees can be spread apart or close together. The former will stretch your hips flexors more.

☞ Now, gently lower your upper body until your forehead touches the floor. Simultaneously, gently stretch your ass towards your heels. Relax your arms and allow them to lie on the floor, either in front of you or behind.

Chapter 6

The Feet and Ankles

Our feet and ankles are key areas of the body, often overlooked in exercise routines. Our feet are where we ground ourselves, where we make contact with the earth. If there's a lot of holding in our feet and ankles it will not be easy to feel grounded and safe in our body. It will also be difficult to discharge emotional stress back to the ground. Releasing the charge from our feet and ankles is a key element of Grounding - see Chapter 2.

The Basic Ankle Stretches

These are 3 pairs of walking around exercises that will really support you to release the holding in your feet and lower legs. They're usually performed one after the other.

Equipment: The room you practice in should have an accessible wall or something similar that you can hold onto for support. This is needed for the middle part of each stretch.

Timing & Repetitions: Begin with a 90-second ding and work up towards 4 or 5 minutes. Doing reps will increase the release, but it's not compulsory, especially when you're new to this exercise. However, if you see that a lot is being released, and you want to go deeper, then try 3 reps with a 2-minute ding. That will take a total of 36 minutes.

Warm Up, Rest Position & Closing: You don't need to be warmed up before beginning this exercise. At each ding, before moving on to the next stretch in the sequence, walk normally for a few seconds. To close, simply sit or lie down for 3-5 minutes, breathing and feeling your body. Alternatively, you might like to shake your body first (5.4).

Notes: Each of the following stretches uses the same basic format. Before starting Ankle Stretch 1, walk slowly around the space for one ding, breathing through the mouth and staying really conscious of your body. At the ding, you move into Ankle Stretch 1 (see below). With the next ding, you walk normally for a few steps and then go into Ankle Stretch 2. With the next ding, once again you walk a few steps normally and then go into Ankle Stretch 3, and so on.

Roughly in the middle of each stretch, for around 20-30 seconds, you do the following. Make gentle contact with a wall or something similar, so that you have support. Stop walking, close your eyes, check your knees are slightly bent, breathe deeply through the mouth, and really feel inside, all the time maintaining the stretch to the max. Feel right into any areas that are starting to ache. Facing your feelings in this way is really healthy. Stay like this for 20-30 seconds and then, maintaining the stretch, open your eyes, walk on and continue until the ding sounds.

6.1 Ankle Stretch 1 - Walk on Toes

Method:

☛ Walk on your toes, keeping your heels as far off the ground as you can. Don't let them down until the ding sounds. Don't forget to stop in the middle as described above.

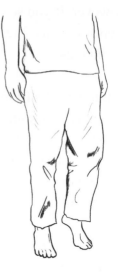

6.2 Ankle Stretch 2 - Walk on Heels

Method:

☛ Walk on your heels, keeping your toes high in the air.

6.3 Ankle Stretch 3 - Walk on Insides of Feet

Method:

☛ Walk on the insides of your feet, keeping the outsides of your feet as far off the floor as you can.

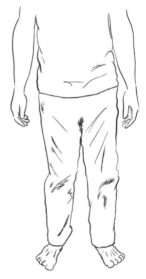

6.4 Ankle Stretch 4 - Walk on Outsides of Feet

Method:

Walk on the outsides of your feet, keeping the insides up off the floor.

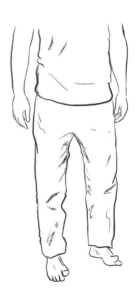

6.5 Ankle Stretch 5 - Twist Legs Outward

Method:

☞ Walk around twisting your lower legs outwards, causing your toes to point apart while your heels come together, like a penguin. Twist your legs to the max. Some people can even get their toes to point slightly backwards. Keep twisting in this way until the ding sounds - don't slacken off.

☞ During the standing part of the stretch, you can use the friction of the floor to increase the twist.

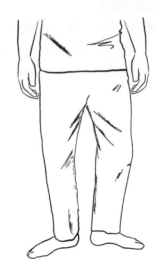

6.6 Ankle Stretch 6 - Twist Legs Inward

Method:

☞ Walk around twisting your legs inwards, so that your toes come together and your heels move apart.

Remember in the middle of each of these exercises to stop, support yourself and increase the stretch, as described above.

Now let's look at a few more ways that you can usefully stretch your ankles. The first three of these exercises are taken from the work of Alexander Lowen.

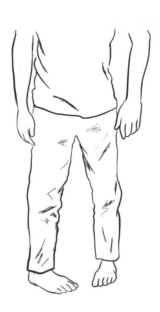

6.7 Ankle Flexing

Timing & Repetitions: Use a 30-second ding to begin with and perform 3 reps.

Warm Up, Rest Position & Closing: It's good to have your legs and feet at least a little warmed up before starting. Use Rest Position 5.1 for one ding in between reps. To close, simply lie flat out in Rest Position 5.3 for at least 3 dings, breathing and feeling your body.

Method:

- Lie on your back in Rest Position 5.1. Remain in this pose for one ding, breathing and feeling your body. Your eyes may be open or closed.
- Now, lift both legs so that your upper legs are at right angles to your body and your knees are bent at 45 degrees.
- Keeping your legs steady, flex both feet up and down from the ankles, as far as they will move. Move them together, following the breath if you desire.
- At the ding, return to 5.1.
- Perform 3 reps of the same exercise, breathing and feeling into your feet and ankles the whole time.
- To close, lie in Rest Position 5.3 for 3 dings.

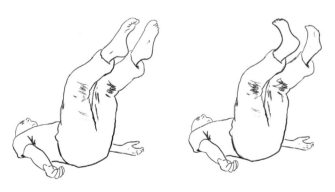

6.8 Ankle Rotation

Timing & Repetitions: Use a 20-second ding to begin with and perform 3 reps.

Warm Up, Rest Position & Closing: It's good to have your legs and feet at least a little warmed up before starting. Use Rest Position 5.1 for one ding in between reps. To close, simply lie flat out in Rest Position 5.3 for at least 3 dings, breathing and feeling your body.

Method:

- Lie on your back in Rest Position 5.1. Remain in this pose for one ding, breathing and feeling your body. Your eyes may be open or closed.
- Now, lift both legs up so that your upper legs are at right angles to the body and your knees bent at 45 degrees, as in 6.7.
- Keeping your legs steady, rotate both of your feet from the ankle in as wide a circle as you can.
- Rotate in one direction, clockwise or anticlockwise, for one ding, and then rotate in the other for one ding.
- When you've rotated your feet in both directions, for one ding each, then return to Rest Position 5.1 for one ding.
- Complete 3 reps.
- To close, lie down in Rest Position 5.3 for 3 dings.

6.9 Foot Shaking

Timing & Repetitions: Use a 20-second ding to begin with and perform 3 reps.

Warm Up, Rest Position & Closing: It's good to have your legs and feet at least a little warmed up before starting. Use Rest Position 5.1 for one ding in between reps. To close, simply lie flat out in Rest Position 5.3 for at least 3 dings, breathing and feeling your body.

Method:

☛ Lie on your back in Rest Position 5.1. Remain in this pose for one ding, breathing and feeling your body. Your eyes may be open or closed.

☛ Now, lift your right leg, such that it is in the same position as in 6.7 and 6.8 above. Leave your left leg down. Keeping your right leg fairly steady, shake your right foot vigorously from the ankle in all directions until the ding.

☛ At the ding, lower your right leg back down, bring your left leg up and shake the left foot as above.

☛ At the next ding, lie with both legs in Rest Position 5.1 for one ding.

☛ Repeat three times.

☛ To close, lie back in Rest Position 5.3 for 3 dings.

6.10 C-Walk Ankle Stretch

The C-Walk, or Crip Walk, is an urban dance movement created by the Crips street gang of Los Angeles. It is also an excellent way of taking out holding in your ankles and lower legs. Check YouTube for lessons on How to Do It.

Chapter 7

The Legs

Like the ankles and feet, the legs are both important and largely over-looked. And not just because, without them, we could not easily get around. Most therapies that work with the body don't give anywhere near enough attention to the legs. Not only do they usually have a huge reservoir of charge, especially the backs of the legs. But also, if the legs are energetically clear, then they really allow us to discharge a lot of daily stress. Once our legs are relatively free of holding we can be much more functional, even when our lives are really intense.

One way of looking at the trunk of the body is as a container for our main organs. Our heart, liver, kidneys, adrenals and more are all located in the trunk of the body. A Balinese energy master I trained with for some years used to say that to clear all the negative energies from the organs of the upper body would be many lifetimes work. However, to get the legs clear was a far more practical proposition. Once the legs are clear, a lot of stuck energy in the upper body can simply discharge back to earth.

As mentioned above, the legs are usually riddled with holding pat-terns, especially the backs of the legs. In truth, the whole back of the body, from the heels up to the neck is a vast dumping ground for our ego. All the stuff we want to keep hidden, all the feelings we haven't expressed - it's all in there.

Something I've noticed over the years of working with people is that men seem to have considerably more holding than women in the backs of the legs (also the pelvic floor - see next chapter). So, if you're a guy do make sure that you really do these exercises thoroughly. And if you're a woman, and they don't seem too challenging, don't be concerned.

Let's look at some great exercises to help us get our legs clear. Some of these exercises will inevitably work other areas of our body too. This is fine.

Classic Leg Stretches

Here is a series of fairly well-known leg stretches that you can do individually, or as a series, moving from one to another with a brief rest period in between. It's okay to close your eyes while performing these stretches, if you prefer. Breathe in and out through the mouth throughout. Keep your awareness in your body and endeavour to fully maintain the stretch until the ding.

Timing & Repetitions: I recommend setting a dinger for 30-60 seconds and seeing how you get on. You can work up the length of time to 2 minutes or higher, though I usually recommend people to not go above 2 minutes but rather to do extra reps instead. I recommend that you do at least 3 reps.

Warm Up, Rest Position & Closing: It's great to have your body at least a little warmed up before starting. If you're doing these exercises as a sequence, use 5.1 as a Rest Position. Begin with it and return to it after each exercise. Do the exercise for one ding and then return to 5.1 for one ding.

7.1 Leg Stretch 1

Method:

- Begin in Rest Position 5.1 for one ding.
- Then, stretch your legs towards the ceiling, trying to keep them dead straight through the knees and at right angles to the trunk of your body.
- The soles of your feet should be horizontal.
- Keep the stretch going until the ding, then return to Rest Position 5.1.

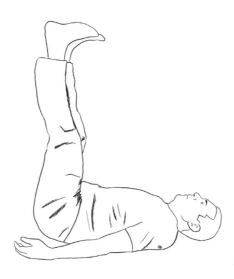

7.2 Leg Stretch with Toe Hold

Method:

- ☛ Bring legs off the floor with knees bent.
- ☛ Reach up and gently take your big toes in your hands.
- ☛ Keeping hold of your toes, gently stretch your legs as straight as you can.
- ☛ Maintain this stretch until the ding, then return to Rest Position 5.1.

7.3 Thigh Stretch

Method:

- ☛ Lift legs as in Leg Stretch 1 above, ensuring that your legs are straight through the knees and at right angles to the body. Now, widen your legs to the sides, creating a 3-way stretch.
- ☛ Maintain this stretch until the ding, then return to the Rest Position 5.1.

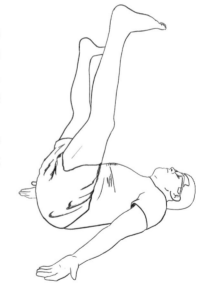

7.4 Leg Stretch with Arms Reaching

Method:

- Note that this particular stretch is usually more powerful when done with eyes open and focused on a point on the ceiling.
- Lift legs as in Leg Stretch 1 above. Simultaneously raise your arms towards the ceiling, keeping your palms facing each other and shoulder-width apart.

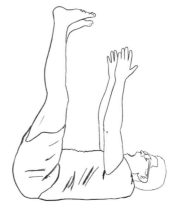

- Keeping your back and head on the mat, reach up with your arms as far as possible, all the time maintaining the leg stretch too.
- Maintain this stretch until the ding, then return to Rest Position 5.1.

7.5 Leg Stretch, Arms Reaching with Release

Method:

- This exercise needs to be done in an environment where you can make noise.
- Lift legs and arms as in 7.4 above.
- Keeping your eyes open and focussed on a point on the ceiling, begin to say the words "Give it to me!" in the language you spoke as a child. Allow yourself to free

associate, expressing anything that comes into your mind without censoring.

- ☛ This exercise often provokes deep emotions. Assuming you're in a place where you can make sound, allow yourself to go into it as fully as you feel comfortable.
- ☛ Maintain the stretch, and the expression, until the ding and then return to Rest Position 5.1.

This completes the series of leg stretches that may easily be run together. If you have been doing them, or some of them, as a series, then it's important to close the series properly. Allow your body to stretch out fully in 5.3 for at least 5 minutes.

Notes and Variations for the Classic Leg Stretches

- When you are experienced with these stretches, it is fine to stop moving back to the Rest Position in between each stretch. It's important to begin and end the sequence with it, but you can move from one leg stretch into the next.
- To add variety, you can experiment with placing a bolster, such as a firm, rolled-up yoga mat, underneath your tailbone while doing this series.
- To allow some extra release at the end of the sequence, put your body into the final Psoas Release (8.7-3) position for 5 to 10 minutes. After this time, go straight into 5.3 and relax for a similar length of time.

We will now look at some other leg stretches.

7.6 The Chair (aka The Wall Sit)

This is a great, intense stretch for the backs of the legs and lower back in particular.

Important: If you have issues with your legs or back, do treat this exercise with respect. Check in with a medic if you're concerned.

Equipment: You will need a free stretch of wall to sit against. There should be nothing fixed to the wall that your ass could rest upon, such as an architrave. Make sure that your feet feel firm on the floor - so that you can't slide down.

Timing & Repetitions: Start with just 30 seconds and work up to 5 minutes. Do 3 repetitions, using the Arch pose (4.1) to rest and integrate in between.

Warm Up, Rest Position and Closing: No warm-up is needed. Hang forwards into the Arch pose (4.1) between dings. To close, return to the Arch pose for one ding and then sit or lie down for a few minutes.

Method:
☛ Sit unsupported against a wall. Your knees should form a right angle, so that your upper legs are horizontal, parallel to the floor, and your lower legs are vertical, ankles beneath your knees. Your back and the back of your head should be flat on the wall. Your

arms are rested with your hands gently resting in your lap, similar to a meditation pose. Do not apply pressure to your upper legs with your hands. The posture looks just like sitting on a chair, but without the chair!

☛ Keeping your eyes open, breathe deeply in and out through the mouth. Feel your body, in particular the muscles that are getting activated.

☛ Complete one ding, then gently push out from the wall and hang forwards in the Arch pose for one ding.

☛ Complete 3 reps of these two postures.

☛ To close, simply sit or lie down for at least 3 minutes, remaining, as always, breathing and feeling your body.

☛ Note: While this exercise is less intense if you bring your back higher up the wall, personally, I recommend that you keep your ass at knee height.

☛ Note: This pose may well bring on spontaneously shaking in the legs. This can be a little scary at first, but rest assured that it's good, and simply a deeper release taking place. Keep breathing deeply through the mouth.

☛ Be aware that for most people this posture is very intense, especially at first. It's fine to start with just 15 seconds if needed and slowly work the time up.

7.7 The Crouch

Crouching down is practised as part of daily life throughout much of Africa and is very healthy for your lower back and your legs.

Timing & Repetitions: Begin with a 30-second ding and work up to 5 minutes. 3 reps is good. Rest in the Arch position (4.1) for one ding in between reps.

Warm Up, Rest Position & Closing: No warm-up is needed. Use the Arch pose (4.1) as a Rest Position between reps. To close, sit or lie down for a minute or two.

Method:

- Stand upright with your feet flat on the floor.
- Slowly drop your ass as low as you can, keeping your heels on the floor. At the same time, reach out with your arms, keeping them horizontal, with palms facing down. Hold the position, breathing fully in and out through the mouth, for one ding.
- At the ding, come into the Arch pose (4.1) for one ding. Repeat 3 times.
- To close, sit or lie down in 5.3 for a minute or two.

7.8 Toe Crouch

Timing & Repetitions: Begin with a 20-second ding and work up to 3 minutes. 3 reps is good. Rest in the Arch position (4.1) for one ding in between reps.

Warm Up, Rest Position & Closing: No warm up is needed. Use the Arch pose (4.1) as a Rest Position between reps. To close, sit or lie down for a minute or two.

Method:

- Stand upright with your feet flat on the floor.
- Lift your heels and at the same time drop your ass, reaching out with your arms forwards, palms facing down.
- Endeavour to get your upper legs horizontal, not lower and not higher. If this is not possible for you, don't worry - this is an intense pose. Breathe deeply in and out through the mouth and really feel your body.
- At the ding, come into the Arch pose (4.1) for one ding. Repeat 3 times.
- To close, sit or lie down for a minute or two.

7.9 Trust Reach

Timing & Repetitions: Begin with a 20-second ding and work up to 3 minutes. 3 reps is good. Rest by standing upright, with a slight bend in the knees, for one ding in between reps.

Warm Up, Rest Position & Closing: No warm-up is needed. Stand upright, with a slight bend in the knees, as a Rest Position between reps. To close, simply sit or lie down for a minute or two.

Method:

- ☛ Stand upright on one leg, with your other leg bent 90 degrees at the knee.
- ☛ Lean forwards, reaching with your arms, until your fingertips rest on the floor. Now lift your bent leg as high as you can.
- ☛ Hold this pose, breathing and feeling, for 1 ding.
- ☛ At the ding, come back upright on both feet for 1 ding.
- ☛ Repeat the exercise using the other leg and returning to standing for one ding afterwards.
- ☛ Repeat this sequence three times.
- ☛ To close, simply sit or lie down for a minute or two.

7.10 Get Off My Back - Leg Version

This exercise can create a great release for the lower back as well as the legs.

Important: This is an intense release exercise and it needs to be treated with respect. If you have leg or back issues, check in with a medic before commencing. Try a few practice backward kicks before going fully into it, to ensure you're not going to hurt yourself.

Music: Playing loud aggressive music will likely support the release but is not essential.

Environment: This exercise should be practised in an environment where you can make a lot of noise.

Timing & Repetitions: Begin with a 30-second ding and work up to 2 minutes. There's no need for reps.

Warm Up, Rest Position & Closing: Make sure you are warmed up before you begin. There's no Rest Position. To close, come into Child Pose (5.5) and rest there for at least 2 minutes, before coming into Lying Down Pose (5.3) for another 3 minutes.

Method:

☛ Begin in Tabletop pose, with your palms and lower legs flat on the floor, and your back horizontal. Your upper legs and arms should be close to vertical, with your hands underneath your shoulders. Ensure there is nothing behind you that you could possibly hit when you begin kicking.

☛ Lifting one leg, kick backwards and slightly upwards while saying out loud "Get off my back," in the language you spoke as a child. Free associate, saying out loud any words that come into your mind.

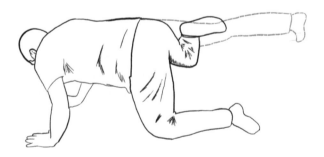

☛ Alternate between legs, giving 2 or 3 kicks with each, before swapping over. Continue expressing and free-associating.

☛ Do this exercise for around 1 to 2 minutes, or until you feel genuinely empty. Ensure that you keep expressing throughout. It's important to make sound with this exercise, even if not distinct words. Grunts are fine.

☛ When complete, slowly come into Child Pose (5.5) for at least 2 minutes, keeping your eyes closed, breathing and feeling your body. Then turn over into and lie in 5.3 for a further 3 minutes.

☛ With this exercise, it is not usually necessary to do repetitions. It's better to try and exhaust yourself totally in one burst.

Chapter 8

The Pelvis

The whole pelvic area is hugely important in Bioenergetics. This part of our body is the seat of both our sexual aliveness and much of our natural vitality.

Any level of sexual trauma, or any feeling of "not being okay" about our sexuality, tends to create holding in the pelvic area. And, because the pelvis is so important, these blocks can create disproportionately large negative effects within us. Our sense of natural aliveness may be much lower than it should be. Or we may find our mind becoming overly sexualised, while our body remains a no-go area where we simply block out natural feelings.

The reality is that nearly everyone on our planet has been brought up in a sexually repressive environment, and this is not natural. Many cultures and religions actually perpetuate themselves by inducing guilt and shame about sexuality in the young.

To really heal on a deep level, at some point you will have to work with sexuality. It is such a major issue that it really cannot be avoided. Otherwise, it will simply become a huge "elephant in the room," an unacknowledged but ever-present block, deeply affecting our life.

Fortunately, working with the pelvis is a big part of Bioenergetics. There are many exercises that will gradually free this area up and leave you feeling liberated. Over time, you will find yourself better able to both hold safe boundaries for yourself and to open up to new experiences if you wish.

When we work with the pelvic area, the focus is slightly different from many of the other areas of the body. There is even more emphasis on breathing and feeling. You really cannot do these exercises like an automaton and expect good results. You will need to keep feeling into the whole pelvic area throughout. The approach has to be more subtle than in other chapters, more *yin*. In the following exercises, practice really keeping your awareness in the pelvic area, gently striving to feel as much as you can.

Pelvis Release Sequence

These three exercises, 8.1 - 8.3, may be done individually. But they are more effective when done in sequence with no gap in between, so that is how I will present them here. They are done with eyes closed, and the first two require you to move your pelvis in time with the breath.

Equipment: These exercises are done lying down and you will need a surface that is firm but not uncomfortable. Two or three yoga mats, one on top of the other, works well for most people.

Music: It can be good to play music for this sequence of exercises. Gentle, oceanic music for 8.1; music with a slight beat for 8.2; and uplifting dance music with a distinct beat for 8.3. Ensure that you create a playlist in advance so that you don't need to change the music manually as you go along.

Environment: The final stage of this sequence, 8.3, goes deeper when you allow yourself to make natural sounds. These may become quite loud. So, ideally, choose an environment where this will not disturb others.

Timing & Repetitions: I recommend starting with a 7-minute ding. That means you will perform each of the three exercises for 7 minutes, taking a total of 21 minutes. You can increase or decrease this as desired once you are experienced. No repetitions are required for this sequence.

Warm Up, Rest Position & Closing: There's no need for any warm-up. As you move from one position straight into the next, neither is there a need for Rest Positions. To close, you simply lie flat out with limbs outstretched (5.3) and totally relax for at least 10 minutes, remaining, as ever, feeling your body.

8.1 Pelvic Rotation

Method:
- ☛ Lie back on the floor in Rest Position 5.1. Have your eyes gently closed and your arms relaxed by your sides, palms facing up. The back of your head should be on the mat.
- ☛ Following the breath, gently rotate your pelvis forwards and backwards, keeping your tailbone on the floor the whole time. This means, as you breathe in, you raise your lower back off the mat, keeping your tailbone down and taking your perineum (the point between your anus and your genitals) down towards

the mat. As you breathe out, you reverse this, bringing your lower back down and your perineum upwards.

- From the side, it would seem that your pelvis is gently rotating backwards and forwards, using your tailbone as a fulcrum. It's important that your tailbone stays on the mat the whole time.
- Stay following the breath with this movement and remain feeling into your pelvic area until the ding.

8.2 Pelvic Lift and Lower

Method:

- When the ding sounds, gently stop the rotation and change to the following exercise. Breathing in, gently lift your pelvis off the mat about 5 cms (2 inches), then lower it slowly back down as you breathe out. Continue with this until the ding.
- **Important:** Remember that this is a gentle exercise. It's not a yogic lift or gym exercise. It's important not to lift your pelvis more than 5 cm (2 inches) off the floor. Remember to follow the breath and to really feel into the pelvis as it moves. This act of feeling is the most important aspect. The exercise is subtle, but over time it can create a very deep release.

8.3 Pelvic Bumping

Method:

- When the ding sounds, you move straight into this exercise. It is actually very similar to 8.2, but with one important difference. Breathing in, lift your pelvis about 2 inches from the mat, exactly as in 8.2. When you breathe out, however, just allow your pelvis to drop back down to the mat with a little bump.

- It's important not to control the descent of the pelvis. You lift on the in-breath, and on the out-breath, you simply let go.

- After a minute or two, you can experiment with changing the speed with which you lift and drop the pelvis. You no longer need to follow the breath. Try increasing the speed that you bump the pelvis to the maximum you can do. To support this, you can play a pumping piece of dance music. You should have this ready before you start so you don't need to interrupt the exercise.

- If you are in an environment where you can make sound, then allow yourself to do so. Practice simply opening your mouth, feeling into your throat, and allowing a sound to come out unscripted. This can really deepen the release and you may be surprised at the sounds that come out of you!

- Once you are experienced with this exercise, you will find that there is a point at which the pelvis seems to start moving by itself. Try to just allow this if it starts to happen. Our pelvis actually has a lot of natural intelligence and its movements can create deep healing without our thinking mind needing in any way to be involved.

☛ When the ding sounds, slowly stop the bumping movement and allow your body to relax. Stretch your arms and legs right out and relax totally for at least 10 minutes. Breathe naturally and stay present in your body, feeling what's happening.

That completes the Pelvis Release Sequence. Now let's look at more exercises we can do to release tension from the pelvic area.

8.4 Pelvic Floor Opening Sequence

Opening the muscles of the pelvic floor is important. Men in particular often have their pelvic floor closed. When the muscles in the pelvic floor are tight, the person often experiences themselves as needy. They instinctively want to cling on to others, literally or metaphorically, as a means to discharge excess energy. When the pelvic floor is more open, it is easier for excess energy to simply flow to earth. We experience more freedom to simply be ourselves and less a sense of having to constrain who we are to fit in with society or to stay in a relationship.

The 4 positions in this sequence are all found in different parts of this book. They are drawn from the work of Alexander Lowen, although I have created this sequence myself. Find images of the postures in the individual chapters where they appear.

Equipment: You will need a rolled-up yoga mat, or similar, to act as a bolster. It should be sufficiently firm to raise your lower back off the floor, while also allowing your tailbone to reach the floor within a minute or so of lying on it.

Timing & Repetitions: Start with a 1-minute ding. Decrease this if any of the positions in the sequence cause excessive discomfort.

Over time, you can increase up to 2 or 3 minutes. It's good to do 3 repetitions.

Warm Up, Rest Position & Closing: You don't need to do any specific warm-up for this sequence. There's no Rest Position either. You simply move from one position into the next at each ding. After you've done your reps, to close, you can either lie flat out (5.3) and relax for at least 3 dings, or you can go into the final position from the Psoas Release Sequence (8.7) and allow your body to release for a while. After that, lie flat out and relax for at least 3 dings.

Method:

☞ **Position 1 - DLP (5.2):** Lie on the floor in the Diamond Leg Posture, but with the bolster under your lower back. Close your eyes, keep your attention on your body and breathe quite deeply through the mouth. Remain in this posture for one ding, relaxing as much as you can. Remember that the bolster you use should allow your tailbone to rest on the floor, if not straight away, then shortly after lying over it. Remain in this posture for one ding.

☞ **Position 2 - Reverse Lower Back Stretch (9.3):** Now, lift your ass and move the bolster from under your lower back to right under the tailbone. Then bring your tailbone back down on top of it. Bend your knees and gently bring them towards your chest, bringing your hands around to clasp them. Your knees and ankles should be gently touching. On the out-breath, gently pull your knees a little more towards your body, softly compressing your belly. Take care with this posture, especially if you have any history of pain or injury in your belly or intestines. Remain in this posture for one ding.

☞ **Position 3 - Leg Stretch 1 (7.1):** Relax your arms and bring them back to your sides. Straightening your legs, bring them up at right angles to the trunk of the body, straightening through the knees as much as you can. The soles of your feet are horizontal and facing the ceiling. If spontaneous shaking starts to occur then allow it. It's good! Maintain this posture for one ding, continuously trying to keep your legs as straight through the knees as possible.

- ☛ **Position 4 - Thigh Stretch (7.3):** Keeping your legs vertical and straight, now stretch them wide, into a V shape, creating a 3-way stretch. Maintain this posture and all 3 directions of stretch for one ding.
- ☛ Complete 3 repetitions.
- ☛ Once the reps are complete, you can either begin resting in 5.3 or first go into the final Psoas Release posture (8.7 #3) to allow some extra release to take place. When you are ready to rest, simply lie flat out with limbs outstretched (5.3) for at least 3 dings, breathing gently and staying present in your body.

8.5 Wah-Wah Pelvic Release

So named because of the characteristic "Wuh" sound that participants make. This is a great exercise that is intended to be done standing up. You can do it on your own, with a partner, or as a group, standing in a circle.

Music: It can be good to play some uplifting or sexy dance music with a distinct beat in the background.

Timing & Repetitions: Start with 10 minutes. When experienced at how the release feels, you can increase or decrease that time to suit. It's fine to go up to 60 minutes if you wish. No repetitions are needed.

Warm Up, Rest Position & Closing: It's good to be at least a little warmed up before starting this exercise. There is no Rest Position. To close, I recommend you simply lie down (5.3) for at least half the time you did the exercise for, to integrate. Alternatively, you may prefer to shake (5.4) first.

Method:

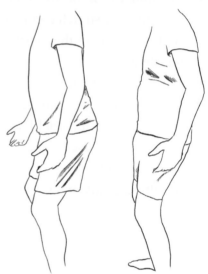

- Stand upright with your feet about shoulder-width apart and your knees a little bent. Try to have the outsides of your feet roughly parallel.
- Now, flick your pelvis forwards from the hips, as you breathe out, simultaneously making the sound "Wuh!"
- As you breathe in, bring your pelvis fully back, without sound.
- Ensure that your back remains loose, but also relatively static. It is not that most of your body is rocking back and forth. It is just your pelvis and upper legs that move. This can be tricky at first, especially if your lower back is quite tense, but you will get the knack of it if you stick with it.
- Continue for at least 10 minutes, ensuring that you make this "Wuh" sound with each forward movement. Stay present in your body while you're doing it.
- To close, simply lie down (5.3), relax and stay breathing and feeling your body for 10 minutes. You may add a stage of Shaking (5.4) before this if you wish.

This exercise can also be done with a partner, facing each other and moving your pelvises in sync. It's good to keep eye contact if you like to create more energy between you and make it more intense.

It can also be done as a group. You stand in a circle, facing inwards, holding hands and moving your pelvises in sync with each other. To increase the experience, make eye contact with someone across the circle.

8.6 Pelvic Hold-up

This is another great release pose for the pelvis and also the legs and lower back.

Timing & Repetitions: Start with one minute and work upwards as you feel. It's good to do 3 reps with a rest period of one ding in between each.

Warm Up, Rest Position & Closing: You don't need to be warmed up to perform this exercise. Begin in Rest Position 5.1 and return to this posture for one ding in between each rep. To close, simply lie down in Rest Position 5.3 for several dings, relaxing and feeling your body.

Method:
- Start in Rest Position 5.1.
- Now, raise your tailbone about 3 inches (75 mm) off the floor, simultaneously pointing your toes so your

heels come off the floor as well. Breathe in and out through the mouth.

- Hold the position for one ding, breathing quite deeply and feeling your body.
- Return to 5.1 for one ding.
- Complete 3 repetitions.
- To complete, lie stretched out in Rest Position 5.3. Close your eyes and stay present in your body.

8.7 Psoas Release Sequence

This fairly well-known sequence of movements is great for releasing tension from the Psoas muscles and other hip flexors. These muscles are particularly associated with sexual trauma or sexual repression, but in reality tension from any origin may tend to accumulate here. The aim is to bring your body into a state of spontaneous release, which usually manifests as involuntary shaking, and then to allow that release to continue for as long as it wants.

Music: Gentle, oceanic music can support the release with this exercise.

Timing & Repetitions: Start with a one minute ding and work up to two minutes. It's not necessary to do repetitions with this sequence, but if you have time you may remain in the final posture for up to 20 minutes, or even longer.

Warm Up, Rest Position & Closing: You don't especially need to be warmed up for this series of postures. This sequence begins in Rest Position 5.2, Diamond Leg Pose (DLP). You also return to this posture for one ding in between Postures #1 and #2. To close the sequence, simply lie flat out in Rest Position 5.3 for at least 5 dings.

Method:

☞ Begin in 5.2 for one ding.

☞ **Posture #1** - At the ding, lift your tailbone about 2 inches (5 cm) off the floor and keep it up. Do not lift it more than this. At the same time, squeeze your shoulder blades towards each other, taking your upper back slightly off the floor. Breathe in and out quite deeply through the mouth and feel into your pelvis, especially the area around the hips. Maintain this posture for 3 dings.

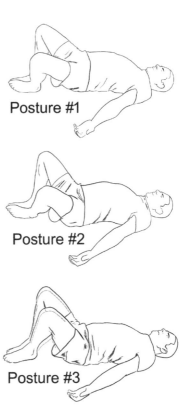

Posture #1

Posture #2

Posture #3

☞ At the third ding, lower your tailbone to the floor, relax your shoulder blades and return to Rest Position 5.2 for one ding.

☞ **Posture #2** - Keeping your tailbone on the floor, and the soles of your feet softly pressed together, gently lift your knees upwards. Note that you need to keep the outsides of the soles of your feet touching, so your knees probably will not move so much. Maintain this gentle stretch, again breathing in and out through the mouth quite deeply, for 2 dings.

☞ At the second ding, come straight into Posture #3. No Rest Position is needed this time.

☞ **Posture #3** - Lift your knees and alter your leg position so that the soles of your feet are now flat on the floor. Your feet should be gently touching or no more than about one inch (2.5 cm) apart. Your knees should be high and gently touching. Now, keeping the soles of your feet flat on the floor, allow your knees to slowly fall outwards, feeling for a point where spontaneous shaking starts to take place. This has to be done softly and with awareness. Really feel into your legs as the knees slowly separate. Your feet should remain planted flat on the floor. If the inner part of the soles come off the floor, then you have moved your knees too far.

☞ It may be tricky to find a point where spontaneous shaking begins. You cannot force it. But stick at it and it will happen. It is not something that you can force.

☞ When you do find a point where your body begins to shake of its own accord, then remain in that position and allow this shaking to continue. You may find that it changes as you go along. Perhaps it starts with the legs shaking side to side, and then you find your back wiggling, and then find your ass gently bumping up and down on the floor. Have an attitude of seeking and allowing, rather than trying to make anything happen. Keep your breathing nice and deep, through the mouth, and keep feeling into the pelvic area.

☞ Continue with this posture for 5 dings at least. If you have time you may extend this to 10 dings or even more.

☞ To complete the sequence, you simply stretch out and relax in 5.3. Remain there for at least 10 minutes, breathing naturally and feeling your body.

8.8 Pelvic Bounce Out

This movement is similar to Pelvic Bumping (8.3) but makes use of a small bolster to keep the tailbone off the floor.

Equipment: You will need a firm, rolled-up yoga mat to use as a bolster.

Environment: The ideal environment in which to do this exercise is one where you can make some level of emotional expression noise.

Timing & Repetitions: Start with 3 minutes. As you feel comfortable, or if you feel a lot is trying to shift within you, you can work upwards to even 30 minutes. There are no repetitions with this exercise.

Warm Up, Rest Position & Closing: It is good to be warmed up before beginning this exercise. There is no Rest Position. To close, simply lie back in Rest Position 5.3 for at least 5 minutes.

Method:

- Lie with your back on the floor in Rest Position 5.1 but with the bolster under your tailbone.

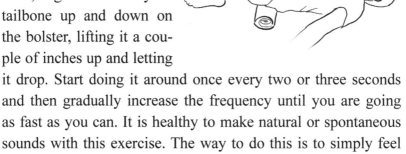

- Now, begin to bounce your tailbone up and down on the bolster, lifting it a couple of inches up and letting it drop. Start doing it around once every two or three seconds and then gradually increase the frequency until you are going as fast as you can. It is healthy to make natural or spontaneous sounds with this exercise. The way to do this is to simply feel into your throat and make a sound without thinking about how it will sound.

- When complete, put the bolster to one side and allow your body to stretch out in Rest Position 5.3. Relax completely. Give yourself at least 5 minutes rest time remembering, as ever, to stay present in your body, feeling what's going on.

8.9 The Pelvic Wave

The Pelvic Wave is a wonderful old exercise that has been a favourite of many Bioenergetic Therapists over the decades and has accrued a variety of names. I call it the Pelvic Wave because I think this one is the most descriptive.

This exercise may be done on its own, or at the end of more intense exercises and sequences, as a way to integrate and rebalance before going into relaxation.

Music: Playing some oceanic music can help you go deeper with this exercise. I frequently use the track *Ocean Lost Wave* by the 5th Galaxy Orchestra.

Timing & Repetitions: Start doing the exercise for 5 minutes and work up to 30 minutes or more. There's no need for repetitions.

Warm Up, Rest Position & Closing: You don't need to warm up. There's no Rest Position. To close, simply sit or lie down, breathing gently through the mouth and feeling your body, for 5 to 10 minutes.

Method:

- Stand upright with your shoulders and arms relaxed and a slight flex in the knees. Your eyes may be open or closed. Breathe through the mouth and feel your body.
- Now, move your pelvis forwards, as though it were being pushed, and allow the rest of your body to simply follow. When your pelvis returns to the back, move it forwards again and continue. The idea is that only your pelvis moves with intention, rather as

though someone is pushing it, and that the rest of your body simply follows along.

- ☛ Try to keep your neck relaxed. When you've got the hang of this exercise, your head will simply flop forwards and back, following the movements of the pelvis.

- ☛ Keep going until the ding. With eyes closed, your body may feel like a piece of seaweed being gently buffeted by the waves of the ocean. It should be very relaxing, though you may also become aware of where tensions are being held in your body.
- ☛ To close, simply sit or lie down for 5 to 10 minutes. Keep your eyes closed, feel your body and breathe naturally.

8.10 Pelvic Flicking

This is a simple pelvic exercise that will increase your pelvic mobility.

Music: Playing a South American or African dance track in the background can support this exercise.

Timing & Repetitions: Start with 1 minute and work up to 5 minutes as you feel. There's no need for repetitions.

Warm Up, Rest Position & Closing: You don't need to be especially warmed up for this exercise. Neither will you need a Rest Position. To close, simply return to standing upright, with knees slightly flexed. Breathe and feel your body for one ding.

Method:

- Stand upright with your eyes open and a little flex in your knees. Have your pelvis cocked slightly backwards.
- Now, flick your pelvis to the left and then to the right, rather like in African dance. Hold each movement for a second or two.
- Continue until the ding, staying in touch with the feeling in your body throughout.
- To close, simply return to the starting position and remain upright, breathing through the mouth and feeling your body.

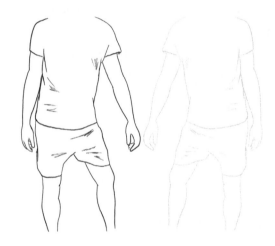

The Belly

In my opinion, the belly is by far the most undervalued area of our energetic anatomy. Its significance can barely be overstated. Many people come to me who have done all manner of therapies. They've tried psychoanalysis, bodywork, energy work, spiritual practice and more. They've done years of work on themselves. Most come because they still feel something huge is missing in their lives. They have created this beautiful personality but somewhere find that it is also a prison. Invariably, they have not properly brought their belly centre into their awareness.

Let's take a look at three reasons why the belly is so important...

- Firstly, it is the most powerful and important somatic centre in primates. It is the central point where everything connects up. If their bodies are to function naturally then animals need awareness in their belly. Even when just walking around, many animals move in a way that constantly brings feeling and energy into their belly. When we witness the fluidity of movement that a big cat has, for example, it's easy to negatively compare our own ponderous and often over-thought way of being. The main difference is that the animal is in its belly. It is occupying its natural power centre.

- Secondly, when you are fully conscious of your belly centre, your body has a far greater capacity to heal itself. The idea of reading books on healing will suddenly seem ridiculous to you. Why give your mind the task of trying to heal you, when this process can more naturally be mediated by your belly centre? When your belly centre is strong and conscious, all your organs can interrelate properly and so natural healing can happen spontaneously, without your mind having to get involved.

- Finally, the belly centre is our natural point of meditation. The very first practice the Buddha gave out, on becoming enlightened some 2,500 years ago, was Vipassana. This practice usually involves sitting, simply witnessing the movement of the belly as we breathe. If we consider the 7 primary somatic centres (often called "chakras"), from the crown of the head to the perineum at the base of the spine, the belly is the first that is totally free of mental control. The heart, for example, is an amazing centre. It enables the experience of unconditional love and cosmic realisation. But it is still within the influence of the mind. This is why people who are centred in the heart, but not the belly, usually need to try and exert a lot of control over their surroundings. They are often very busy with how other people or the world should be. When you get awareness into your belly, then you finally have a point within your own conscious experience that is outside the thinking mind - a point that is outside the prison of thought-dominated experience. The power and potential of this cannot be overstated. No longer are you a slave to egoic thought patterns and behaviours. Anytime you want, you can drop into a space of pure presence and awareness.

These are 3 great reasons to develop more awareness in your belly. Be aware also that the belly is a fiery centre! Yes, it's where we experience the bliss of meditation, but it's also the place from where we can instinctively keep our boundaries safe. It's the somatic centre from where anger is mediated.

This fiery reactivity of the belly centre is usually a concern for our ego-dominated mind. It's always on the lookout for anything which could negatively affect how people perceive us, and this fiery belly centre is a big worry! When you start to work at a belly level you risk being more fiery in life, less concerned about what people think of you, and more determined to not take in others' negativity.

In addition to working our belly centre, several of the exercises below also create an opening at throat level. On an energetic level, there is a hugely important channel between our belly and our throat. When both these centres and the channel between them are open, a natural animal intensity is created in the person. It puts a person "in their power." They will no longer accept second best and will be fearless of speaking their truth.

9.1 Belly Activation Sequence

This series of three practices should ideally be practised sequentially, moving from one straight into the next. It's a great workout for the early morning, but can also be done at other times of day. I don't, however, recommend it late at night. It can awaken a lot of energy and you may find it hard to sleep afterwards.

Equipment: Spit Bucket - A washing-up bowl with tissue in may be useful when doing this exercise. If you feel at all nauseous, which is fairly common, then it's great to have a good spit. Stop the exercise and kneel over the bowl to retch if needed.

Music: None is needed for the First Stage. For the Second Stage, some deep Tibetan chanting can be useful, such as *Yamantaka* by The Gyoto Monks. For the Triple Opener, I recommend you download the *Grunt Track* mentioned in the Resources section of this book.

Timing & Repetitions: You need to devote at least 15 minutes to this whole sequence, and ideally more when you first begin working with it. It doesn't require repetitions.

Warm Up, Rest Position & Closing: No warm-up is needed. The Belly Activation Sequence starts quite gently and then gets more intense. No Rest Position is needed. At the end, however, it is important to give yourself at least 10 minutes downtime to relax, process and come back to yourself. This could be by sitting, by shaking or by simply lying flat out on the floor.

Method:

☛ **First Stage:** Stand upright with your feet spread greater than shoulder-width apart and your knees bent. The outsides of your feet should be roughly parallel and your spine upright, leaning neither backwards nor forwards. This posture is frequently found in martial arts, where it is known as "ma bo," or "Horse Stance." Your eyes may be open or closed, but most people find that eyes closed is easiest to begin with.

☛ Now, remaining in this position but with your body relaxed, start to simply feel into your belly while breathing fairly deeply in and out through the mouth. See if you can find any level of sensation in your belly and, if you can, try to use this as an "anchor," a way to remain present in this area. You may find that you can feel no

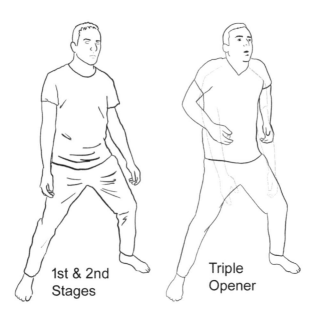

1st & 2nd
Stages

Triple
Opener

sensation in the belly at all. If this happens, don't be discouraged, simply continue trying. Despair is actually one of the feelings commonly repressed around the belly area. Don't give in to it. Continue with this First Stage for around 3-5 minutes.

- **Second Stage:** Remaining in the same posture, on the out-breath, begin to make the lowest sound that you can. As you make this sound in your throat, feel into your belly. If you can create a vibration down your windpipe with this low sound, then this is great. But this is usually difficult when you first start this practice. Remember, the sound is the lowest that your body can physically make. It's not an overtone, it's not a "Hoo" sound (as found in Osho Dynamic Meditation). It is simply the lowest sound that you can make. Continue with this Second Stage for around 5-10 minutes.

- **Third Stage - The Triple Opener:** This exercise involves 3 key areas of your body and I thus call it the Triple Opener. It works your belly, your throat and your shoulders.

☛ Remain in the same posture as the previous two stages. Now, building them up one at a time, add these 2 rhythmic movements -

  ☞ Change the low sound to a distinct, animal-like grunt. Keep the sound as low as you can make it. Feel into your belly with each grunt you make.

  ☞ Lift your shoulders towards your ears and throw them down again, rather like the hard shrug that teenagers give as a form of protest. Make the grunt as your shoulders come down.

  ☞ Some people find it useful to add the following movement - lifting your heels off the floor and bringing them down again. You can experiment with this and see how it feels. If you do choose to do it, then both downward movements - the heels and the shoulders - should happen together with the grunt.

☛ With a little practice, you should be able to maintain these movements in time with each other. Ideally, try to work to a rhythm of slightly faster than one downward movement every second. You can download the "Grunt Track" mp3 for this - see the Resources section at the end of this book.

☛ Important: The trickiest part for most people is the shoulder movement. It's very important that you keep the shoulders moving, not just your arms, and that they travel fully up and down. You may need to practice in front of a mirror to ensure this.

☛ Maintain the Triple Opener for 10-20 minutes.

☛ **Completion:** Have some downtime when you've completed all three stages of the Belly Activation. You can shake, lie down stretched out, or sit in meditation. Give yourself around 10 minutes. Make sure you continue to feel your body while you relax and integrate.

9.2 Hoo Sound Jumping

This intense Bioenergetic exercise was made famous by Osho, the Bhagwan Shree Rajneesh, who included it as the third element of his well known Osho Dynamic Meditation. It's designed to work the belly, the solar plexus and the shoulders and, done correctly, it's a very powerful Bioenergetic practice.

Important: While this is a transformational exercise, some people have reported that it led to them having knee issues after they practised it daily for a number of years. I recommend that if you're concerned about this then you shouldn't perform it more than once a week.

Music: You may like to play Track 3 from Osho Dynamic Meditation while jumping.

Timing & Repetitions: Traditionally, this exercise goes on for 10 minutes and there are no reps. However, it is absolutely fine to start with 1 or 2 minutes as long as you ensure that you really do go for it fully and don't slacken off.

Warm Up, Rest Position & Closing: There's no Rest Position, but it's good to make sure that you're nicely warmed up before starting Hoo Sound Jumping. This means that you need to both stretch and do some level of cardio. Jogging around the room for a little is fine. To close, simply let your body shake (5.4) or relax lying down for at least 5 minutes (5.3).

Method:

☛ Stand upright with your arms raised above your head.

☛ Now, jump up so that your feet leave the floor. When they come back down, ensure that your heels hit the floor, creating a vibration up your legs. That's to say, don't just jump and land on your toes. Your toes can hit the floor first as you come down, but the heels must also make some level of impact.

☛ As your heels come down, focus on your solar plexus and make the sound "Hoo." Continue jumping at a rate of at least one jump every two seconds.

☛ Keep your arms fully raised throughout. Don't allow them to come down.

☛ Note: This exercise can prove to be too much for your knees if you do it for ten minutes every day, as many Osho followers found out as they grew older. If you're concerned that it's too much for your joints, then you can also lift your heels and bring them down, but keep your toes on the floor throughout.

☛ Also note: This exercise is traditionally done with eyes closed. If you find yourself moving around the room a lot, as is common when you really go for it, ensure that the space is safe for you to do this before you start.

☛ When complete, close by simply sitting or lying down with eyes closed for 5 minutes. Alternatively, you may do some shaking (5.4) before going into relaxation.

9.3 Reverse Lower Back Stretch

This well-known lower back stretch, popular with Alexander Lowen, also works the muscles of the belly, so I'm including it in this chapter. Here we'll do it with a counter-stretch, but you can also do it on its own or with a Rest Position.

Important: Be aware that compressing the belly in this way may not be a good idea if you have any history of stomach or intestinal issues. Check with a suitably qualified medic if needed.

Equipment: You will need a firm, rolled-up yoga mat to use as a bolster.

Timing & Repetitions: Start with one minute and work up or down from that as you feel. Do three reps, remaining in the Rest Position for one ding in between each.

Warm Up, Rest Position & Closing: You don't need to be warmed up for this exercise. In between each rep, move into Rest Position 5.2 but with a bolster planted under your lower back. To close, simply put the bolster to one side and lie down flat out (5.3) for 2 dings.

Method:
☛ Begin by lying down on your back with the soles of your feet planted and your knees up (5.1). Place a bolster, such as a firm rolled-up yoga mat, under your tailbone.
☛ Now, keeping your knees bent, bring them up towards your chest, until they are gently compressing your belly. Bring your hands around to softly hold your knees close to your body.

- Slowly and carefully, pull your knees into your body, gently compressing your belly. Take care with this posture, especially if you have any history of injury or similar in your belly or intestines. Keep your knees and ankles gently touching the whole time.
- Stay in this posture for one ding.
- For the Counter-stretch, bring the soles of your feet back down to the floor where you started. Lift your ass a little and slide the bolster up the body until it's under your lower back. Gently lower your body back down over the bolster, allowing your tailbone to touch the floor. Now, adjust your leg position until you're in the DLP (5.2 with bolster). Remain relaxing in this position for one ding.
- When you've completed 3 reps, simply lie out flat in 5.3 and relax for at least 2 dings.

9.4 Belly Roll Out

This intense posture can really help with any level of anxiety that appears rooted in the belly area. If you are a compulsive snacker then this exercise can really support you.

Important: Be aware once again that compressing the belly in this way may not be a good idea if you have any history of stomach or intestinal issues. This exercise is usually more intense than the Reverse Lower Back Stretch above. Check with a suitably qualified medic if you're at all concerned. If it is your first time doing this posture, be really careful not to overdo it.

Equipment: For this exercise, you will need a Foam Roller. It should be around 6 inches, 150 mm, in diameter.

Timing & Repetitions: Start with one minute and see how that feels. Feel free to increase that up to 10 minutes as you become experienced. No repetitions are needed.

Warm Up, Rest Position & Closing: It's good to be at least a little warmed up before starting this exercise. There is no need for a Rest Position. Spending time closing this posture is particularly important. Make sure that you do this. Lie flat out with your limbs outstretched (5.3). Breathe naturally and stay present in your body. Do this for at least 5 minutes.

Method:

☛ Place the Foam Roller on the floor and lie over it, face down. The roller should push right up into the belly cavity, midway between the bottom of your rib-cage and the hips. Allow your head to face either to the left or to the right. It doesn't matter which.

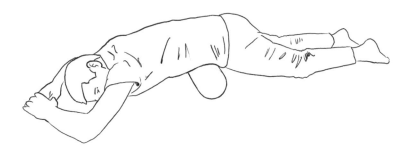

- Breathe through the mouth, in and out, and try to completely relax in this posture. Try to surrender to the feelings that come.
- Roughly midway through, gently turn your head to the other side.
- Maintain for one ding, making sure that you have turned your head once in that time.
- To close, come up gently onto your elbows, put the Roller to one side and turn over. Lie on your back in 5.3 and simply relax for at least 3 dings.

The Lower Back

Of all the areas of the body, the lower back is the place that has by far the most holding and the most dead zones. It is the great dumping ground of our ego. All the trauma our brain has stored away, all the conditioning we've been subjected to, all the feelings we deny or repress - a big chunk of it ends up in the lower back. Yes, holding is distributed across all muscle groups, but the lower back is certainly one area that bears the brunt of it.

One reason for this is likely that we don't easily see our lower back. At an ego level, we are mostly concerned that we look good, and that means a smiling face, an open chest and an upright posture. When we meet the world, they don't see our lower back. And, indeed, it's very hard to see our lower back ourselves. So, this makes it the ideal place to dump all the garbage!

But, of course, just because we don't easily see it, does not mean it's not there. If we don't take steps to open up the muscles of our lower back and allow the feelings held there to once again flow, then this repository of trapped feelings will eventually wreak havoc.

Important: The lower back has muscles that are very easy to pull, possibly because most people have so much repressed there that it's hard to feel what's going on. Be careful with these exercises and do check in with someone medically qualified if at all concerned.

The Bow & Arch (4.1 & 4.2)

The Bow & Arch is an excellent way to progressively open up the lower back. We already covered this exercise extensively in Chapter 4, so please refer back for more information.

10.1 The Lean Over

This exercise creates a deep, gentle stretch in the back. In addition, it can give you a feeling of considerable "let go," a healthy surrender of your mind.

Important: If you have any current or past health issues with your back you will need to check in with a suitably qualified person before undertaking this exercise.

Equipment: Traditionally, in the Alexander Lowen school, this exercise was done by leaning over a piece of equipment called the Bioenergetic Stool. This can be made from a kitchen stool, a rolled-up yoga mat (or similar bolster) and some 1 inch (25 mm) dowel. See the Resources section at the end of the book for more information.

However, I've always believed in making use of things found in the average household, wherever possible. So, for me, I actually prefer practising this exercise over the back of a sofa. In my experience, the average sofa is also more stable than even the best made Bioenergetic Stool. You could also use a heavy-duty sawhorse from a DIY store. Another alternative I've made use of in the past is a section of fence, with a flat or rounded top, of suitable height.

Whichever you choose, you will need a stable and not uncomfortable bar over which you can safely lean backwards. If you're using a sofa, then it is the back of the sofa that you lean over, your feet on the opposite side to the cushions. The height is not critical, but it should be between the height of your crotch and the height of your midback. You will likely need to put a firm cushion on top to ensure that the bar is not uncomfortable. You also need to take responsibility to ensure that you feel safe - that whatever you choose to use, it is not going to fall over. It will be hard to really let go in this exercise if you are worried about the stability of the thing you are leaning over.

I will describe how to do the exercise using a sofa.

Timing & Repetitions: This exercise can be very intense, so I advise starting with just one repetition and a 30-second ding. See how you get on. You can try reps later on when you are more confident.

Warm Up, Rest Position & Closing: It's good to have your body fairly well warmed up before this exercise. To close the exercise, or as a Rest Position if you're doing reps, you make use of a sequence of two postures - Squat and Arch. They are described below. Make sure you use them. It's important with this exercise that you really take care of yourself.

Method:

☞ Move your sofa away from the wall, so that you can stand behind it at a distance of at least two feet (60 cms).

☞ Standing with your back to the rear of the sofa and, using your arms as support, slowly lean backwards over the sofa, keeping at least your toes on the floor.

☞ IMPORTANT - Our backs are very sensitive, so ensure that when you first do this posture, the part of your back which touches

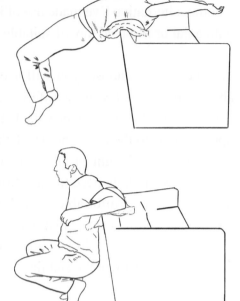

the top of the sofa is the base of the shoulder blades and not lower down. You don't want to put excessive pressure on your lower back when you start this exercise.

☞ Slowly let go control until you are simply hanging over the back of the sofa. You may keep your arms by your side, partly taking your weight, or you may hold them above your head, increasing the stretch.

☞ Close your eyes and breathe deeply through your mouth, feeling your body. Keep your toes on the floor throughout, although you may lift your heels if you wish.

☞ When you hear the ding, come up slowly in the following fashion. First, if your arms aren't already by your side, bring them there and begin to take the weight off your upper body. Now, slowly raise your upper body back towards the vertical. When your upper body is vertical, slowly crouch down, bending your knees, and breathe through the mouth, keeping your awareness on your body the whole time. When you feel stable, straighten your legs and lean forwards into the Arch position and remain there for one ding.

10.2 The Back Roller

This intense exercise can be great to alleviate tension in specific areas of the back or to make use of weaknesses in the back to "shake out" tension.

Important: Using a Foam Roller in this way can be intense. Try it out and if it's painful then leave the exercise, or come back to it later when you've progressed further.

Equipment: You will need a Foam Roller.

Timing & Repetitions: Start with 2 minutes and increase up to 10 minutes. No repetitions are required for this exercise.

Warm Up, Rest Position & Closing: A basic level of warm-up is good. You don't need a Rest Position. To close, simply lie flat on your back and relax (5.3) for 1 ding, remembering, as ever, to keep feeling your body.

Method:
- Lie down on your back in 5.1. Breathe through your mouth gently and feel your body.
- Now, lift your back right off the floor and place the Foam Roller under your hips.

- Next, lift your upper body off the floor, using your elbows and forearms to take your weight at first.
- Now, slowly roll your body so that the roller moves up your back towards your shoulder blades. You may need to move the position of your feet as the roller moves.
- As the roller travels slowly up your back, look for any point where spontaneous shaking begins and then remain on that point until the ding.
- You may have your neck relaxed with your head hanging back, or you may have your head up. Experiment with both to see how they feel.
- When the ding sounds, gently remove the roller and lie back flat on the floor with your legs outstretched (5.3). Breathe gently through the mouth and remain feeling your body for one ding.

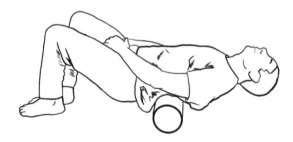

The Shoulders & Upper Back

We are usually more aware of tension that we hold in our shoulders or upper back than in many other areas of our body. In fact, it is a growing awareness of this tension that often leads us into a journey of self-examination. There can be many different psychological roots to the tension we store in these areas. Let's briefly list some of the more significant ones…

- a tendency to keep thinking and doing, as a way to avoid deeper feelings which are repressed.
- a tendency to take on too much responsibility through submerged feelings of guilt.
- an underlying belief that one needs to "please" others - in order to receive love or respect, or to get needs met.
- an incomplete childhood, especially as a teenager, traditionally the time when we throw off the influence of our parents.

Several of these issues are not yet commonly related to shoulder and upper back tension in mainstream psychology. So I would like to briefly expand upon the first in particular.

As well as a physical heart, pumping blood around our body, we also have an "energetic heart," located in the centre of our chest. If you've ever experienced deep grief, it often appears to manifest as a "dam breaking open" in this area. There is a feeling of deep sadness, literally pouring out from the centre of our chest. Many people also experience love as manifesting from this area. Thus it seems that the "heart opens" in this way.

In like manner, the heart also appears to be "kept closed" from the region of the back directly behind the area it appears to open from. That's to say, the area between the shoulder blades. What I see, working with clients, is that if I get them to work the muscles in this part of the body, it begins to mobilise the emotional pain held inside of them.

As children, many of us may have somehow figured out that if we can keep the area between our shoulder blades tense, we can keep our pain hidden away inside of us. It's a form of behavioural denial that, once learned, may well continue for decades without us any longer being aware that we are doing it.

How we keep these muscles tight, and our heart thus closed, is by thinking and doing a lot. There is a circuit in the body from the head, down through the neck and out through the shoulders to the hands. When we spend our waking hours thinking and doing a lot, we keep this circuit active. The area between our shoulder blades remains tense, and our personal pain remains trapped inside of us.

This strategy to keep our pain hidden is obviously not a good long-term proposition. It can also lead to us burning out, through pushing our body and mind to keep busy. So, in this chapter in particular, we will be looking at ways that we can open this area of our body.

Before we get into the exercises themselves, I would briefly like to remind you of two of the principles of Bioenergetics mentioned in Chapter 2 of this book - grounding and compensation. These are particularly significant when seeking to reduce tension in the shoulder area, so please consider rereading these sections.

Now it's time to look at some great exercises specifically aimed at releasing stuck feelings and energy from the shoulders and upper back!

11.1 - 11.4 Shoulder Opening Sequence

This series of 4 exercises works the shoulders and the area between the shoulder blades. It's a great way to get our chest and our heart open, particularly if we've been working hard with our mind all day, perhaps on a computer or a laptop.

Important: If you have any history of shoulder issues then it's important to check with a doctor prior to trying out this sequence.

Timing & Repetitions: Start with a 2-minute ding. Feel free to work up to 5 minutes as you become more experienced with this exercise. This sequence may be done with or without repetitions.

Note: This sequence may either be done walking slowly around, or standing still with knees slightly bent. Doing it standing still is usually more intense.

Warm Up, Rest Position & Closing: It's good to warm your body up at least a little before starting this sequence. There is no Rest Position. To close, you should spend at least 2 dings standing, sitting or lying down, as ever remembering to keep feeling your body.

Method:

☛ Stand upright with your knees slightly bent and your feet about shoulder-width apart, a nice grounded stance. Breathe in and out through the mouth and feel your body for one ding.

☛ **11.1 - Shoulders Forwards:** Now, gently pull your shoulders forwards, as though you are trying to get your shoulders to touch in the centre of your chest. Don't use your hands or arms as levers, but rather allow your arms to follow, resting where they will. The stretch needs to come from the shoulders, not the arms. Keep pulling your shoulders gently together, not allowing any time to relax. Keep a gentle pressure going until the ding. Keep breathing through the mouth.

☛ When the ding sounds, let the stretch go with a deep sigh, throwing your arms down.

☛ **11.2 - Stretch 2 - Shoulders Backwards:** Now perform the reverse stretch. Stretch your shoulders backwards, trying to get your shoulder blades to touch in the upper middle of your back. Perhaps imagine that there's a walnut between your shoulder blades and you really want to crack it! Maintain this stretch, not slackening off for a moment. When the ding sounds, once again release the stretch with a vigorous exhale and a brief throwing down of your arms.

11.1

11.2

- **11.3 - Stretch 3 - Shoulders Up:** This time you're going to bring your shoulders up, as though you're trying to get them to touch your ears. Allow your arms to simply hang where they will. Imagine perhaps that you're auditioning for a part in a Frankenstein movie. Get them as high as you can. Maintain the stretch, until the ding, and then release it as before.

11.3

- **11.4 - Stretch 4 - Shoulders Down:** This final stretch is the opposite of the one before. Stretch your shoulders down towards the floor, rather as though you have heavy weights attached to your wrists. Maintain the stretch until the ding, like before. No resting.

- **Closing:** When the final ding sounds, you can choose to either remain standing or to sit or lie down. If you would like to add some extra release before closing you could spend one or two dings doing Teenager Release (11.5) or Shaking (5.4) before closing. Whichever you choose, make sure you continue to breathe deeply through the mouth and feel your body. So many people simply space out at the end, and this interrupts your integration of the exercise. Remain like this for at least 2 dings.

11.4

- Note: When you are experienced with these stretches, they may be intensified by performing either the Jaw Stretch (13.2) or Fake Smile (13.1) exercises at the same time.

11.5 Teenager Release

Our teenage years are very important. They are the time when we progressively throw off the influence of our parents or other caregivers we may have had during our childhood. Although teenagers are still usually under the control of their parents, they are increasingly ready to drop the behaviours their parents taught them and to begin to forge their own identities. This is an important psychological process and, for many adults, it is not complete.

This lack of completion leaves many people incapable of functioning effectively in hierarchical structures out in the world. Because they still feel like a teenager inside, they feel compelled to react against authority, even when this constantly blocks their development.

Something you will often notice if you pay attention to teenagers, is that they shrug their shoulders hard when asked to do things by their parents. This movement is a gesture of protest. They comply, but they also want to show the adults that they're not happy about it. This shrugging movement is a natural way for them to throw off the influence of parents.

So, in this exercise, you will walk around the room slowly, really lifting your shoulders up to your ears and then throwing them down, with a grunt. Exaggerating the movement in this way creates a release. It should feel good.

When you are experienced with this exercise, you may choose to focus on the final years before leaving the parents behind. To do this you exaggerate the downward throwing of the shoulders and the level of anger still further. It's like you've really had enough of being controlled now!

You can do this as a stand-alone exercise, or go into it after completing the Shoulder Release Sequence above.

Important: If you have any history of shoulder issues, then take responsibility to check in with a doctor prior to doing this exercise.

Music: You don't need to play music with this exercise, but if you do have a loud, rebellious track you can put on in the background, this can help you to get into the feeling. I recommend *Killing in the Name Of*, by Rage Against the Machine. Be aware that you may prefer something rebellious with less swearing in it.

Timing & Repetitions: A good length of time to do this exercise, when you're starting out, is 3 minutes. You can work up to 15 minutes with experience, and especially if you can feel a release taking place. There's no need for repetitions.

Warm Up, Rest Position & Closing: As mentioned, you can use the Shoulder Release Sequence above as a warm-up to this exercise. Otherwise, you simply need to make sure that your upper body is warmed up and fairly loose. There is no Rest Position. To close, lie or sit down for roughly the same length of time that you performed the exercise for.

Method:

☛ Before beginning, walk around the room trying to feel like you're an angry teenager. Perhaps imagine that your Dad is telling you to do your homework, or your Mum is on your back, nagging you to tidy your room. Whatever works for you. Now, as you walk, begin to stamp your feet. Not so hard that you might hurt yourself, but enough so that you can feel it. At the same time, begin to lift your shoulders up towards your ears and, as you put each foot down, throw your shoulders down at the same time. The arms just follow along in this movement. It is the shoulders that do the actual work.

☛ Add also a grunt as you stamp down, just like someone who is angry about being told what to do. Remember, this is not full-blown screaming and shouting, but rather making a physical gesture of protest. You grunt, you stamp your feet and you throw your shoulders down. Stamp your feet and throw your shoulders down at a rate of around once every one or two seconds.

☛ It is also good to make an ugly face. Stick your lower jaw out, screw up your face. Show the world how ugly you can be.

☛ Maintain this posture, sound and movement until the ding sounds.

☛ When the ding does sound, you can either go into relaxation - shaking, sitting or lying down for at least one ding - or you can exaggerate these movements and go into an Expression Stage (see below). If you want to do this Expression Stage, you need to ensure that you are in a space where it will be okay to make loud noise.

☛ **Expression Stage** - Stand still and begin to speed up the shoulder movements, while opening your mouth and allowing a sound to come out. You no longer need to stamp your feet, but your shoulders should move up and down at a rate of about two or three times a second. Try to simply allow sound to come out, rather than forcing it in any way, or thinking about how it should sound. Allow the sound to come, without judgment, and also allow it to get stronger or weaker.

☛ The Expression Stage can continue for two or three minutes. After this, allow yourself to go into relaxation for at least 10 minutes. You can shake your body gently, sit down quietly or lie down on the floor. Whichever you do, ensure that you stay present in your body, feeling what's going on.

11.6 Get Off My Back - Elbows Version

This exercise is similar to 7.10, except that this time you are using your elbows rather than your legs. You will need to be in an environment where you can make sound, ideally a place where it's okay to shout and scream.

Equipment: This exercise is performed kneeling. If the floor is hard, perhaps use a folded over yoga mat to kneel upon.

Music: Not essential, but you may find some loud, rebellious rock music can help you to release.

Timing & Repetitions: Do this exercise initially for 30-60 seconds. You can increase this up to 3 minutes but, once you're confident with it, you will usually find you can get a good release in under one minute. There is no need for repetitions.

Warm Up, Rest Position & Closing: Before performing this exercise, it's important that your shoulders, arms and upper body are warmed up. You could do exercises 11.7 and 11.8 first, or similar. There is no Rest Position. To close, come forwards into Child Pose, 5.5, for at least one ding.

Method:
☛ With your body warmed up, come to kneeling with your ass up away from your heels.

- When you're ready, begin to "dig" your elbows backwards, one after the other, as though there is something on your back and you want to get it off. Do a couple of practice digs first to make sure it's not painful, and then you can really go for it. As you make each dig backwards, say the phrase "Get off my back!" in the language you spoke when you were young. Also free associate. It's important with this exercise that you make sound.

- Note: Often I see people twisting their whole upper body while doing this exercise, but this lessens the release. Your upper body should remain relatively static, without being rigid, and the movement comes from your shoulders.

- Once you get going, you may find that the digging movement almost seems to take you over. It's great when this happens. Allow yourself to shout out anything that's in your mind.

- When the ding goes, bring your ass down to your heels and lean forwards into the Child Pose (5.5), with your feet close together and your knees wide apart. Remain in this posture for at least one ding. Have your eyes closed and breathe and feel your body. Afterwards, you can lie for another ding, either in the foetal position or just flat out on your back (5.3).

11.7 Shoulder Rolling

Timing & Repetitions: Start with 1 minute in each direction. You can work up to 5 minutes. Repetitions are not needed but can be done if you wish.

Warm Up, Rest Position & Closing: No warm-up or Rest Positions are required. To close, simply stand with your knees relaxed and feel your body for 1 ding. Alternatively, you can allow your body to shake for 1 ding.

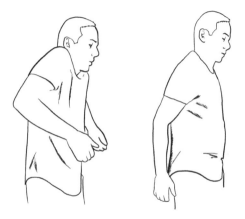

Method:
- ☛ Stand upright in a grounded position with a little flex in your knees, eyes open looking ahead. Breathe deeply through the mouth. Try to engage your belly as you breathe. Deep, constant breathing is very important in this exercise.
- ☛ Now, begin to make circular motions of your shoulders, bringing them up towards your ears and then forwards and down, rotating them in side-view. Make these rotations as wide as you can. The movement is from the shoulders so your arms just follow, relatively relaxed. Continue, breathing deeply through the mouth, for one ding.

- When the ding sounds, stop rotating in that direction and rotate the other way - your arms come up, then move back and down and around. As before, allow your arms to just follow, relaxed. Continue for one ding.
- When the ding sounds, you can close by just continuing to stand, now with your shoulders and arms simply loose and hanging. Have your knees very slightly bent and breathe through the mouth feeling your body.
- As an alternative to closing, you may continue with the next exercise, 11.8, and then close after that.

11.8 Downward Swing Release

This exercise may be done on its own, or you may choose to add it to the end of any of the other shoulder exercises from this chapter that are done standing up.

Timing & Repetitions: Start with 30 seconds and increase that up to 5 minutes as you feel confident. No reps are needed with this exercise.

Warm Up, Rest Position & Closing: You don't need to have a warm-up exercise, but this release can be a good way to complete any of the other exercises in this chapter that are done standing up. No Rest Position is needed. To close, remain standing, with your arms and shoulders now relaxed. Breathe and feel your body.

Method:
- Stand upright with your eyes open and a little flex in your knees.
- Now, lift both arms above your head and stretch them back. Allow your forearms to travel down from your elbows towards

your upper back, as though you're trying to pick up a weight from your shoulders.

☞ When ready, gently throw both arms forwards and down, allowing them to travel fully behind you. When the down-swing is complete, bring them back up again to where they started. Make a sound as you throw your arms down, as though releasing a load from your shoulders.

☞ Continue swinging down and bringing your arms back up for one ding.

☞ Note: As you begin each down-swing, have the feeling that you're throwing something you no longer need off your shoulders. Really let it go.

☞ At the ding, to complete, stand upright with your arms by your sides, relaxed. Have your eyes either open or closed. Breathe through the mouth and feel your body for one ding.

11.9 Reverse Prayer and Reverse Arm-Lift

This pair of exercises are another great way to open up muscles all around the neck and the shoulders. They may be done on their own or added to other exercises, such as the Shoulder Opening Sequence, 11.1 - 11.4. Feel free to complete with some Teenager Release, 11.5, if you desire.

These exercises are "pulsing" exercises. Instead of maintaining a stretch, you maintain a gentle rhythmic pulsing of certain muscle groups.

Timing & Repetitions: Start with a 1-minute ding and work up to a 5-minute ding as you feel confident and ready for a challenge. It's good to do 3 repetitions.

Warm Up, Rest Position & Closing: You don't need a warm-up for this pair of postures. There is also no Rest Position. You simply move from one to the other. To complete, allow your body to gently shake, 5.4, for a couple of minutes, then sit or lie down and relax.

Note: Like 11.1 - 11.4, these exercises may be done walking around, or standing still in a grounded stance (knees slightly bent, feet about shoulder-width apart). Done standing, they are usually more intense.

Method:
☛ We begin with the Reverse Arm-Lift. Standing up, gently clasp your fingers together behind your back, keeping your arms nearly straight but with a small amount of flex in the elbows.
☛ Now, begin to pulse your arms up, as far as you can easily reach, and then back down, to gently tap your tailbone. Breathe deeply through the mouth and feel your body.

- Continue pulsing in this way, fairly quickly, until the ding.
- When the ding sounds, change into the Reverse Prayer position. Lift your arms above your head and press your palms gently together. From the elbows, drop your lower arms so that they are pointing backwards, with the palms still together.
- Now, keeping your upper arms vertical and fairly steady, pulse your lower arms up and back, such that your fingers point back and then point straight up. Point back and then point straight up. Breathe deeply through the mouth and keep feeling your body.
- Continue with this Reverse Prayer pulsing until the ding, then return to Reverse Arm-Lift pulsing.
- Complete 3 reps. You may choose to do one rep walking around, then either one or two standing to increase the intensity of the exercise.
- To close, stand and do the Shaking posture, 5.4, for a couple of minutes, remembering to keep breathing deeply in and out through the mouth. Then either sit down or lie down for 5 minutes, closing your eyes and feeling your body.

Chapter 12

The Neck & Throat

The neck and throat are key areas of our anatomy in psychological terms. The modern world, with its preponderance of screens and keyboards, has progressively become more and more "thought-based." More than ever, we tend to live in our heads, thinking our way through life. But our body often has feelings contrary to the mind's ideas of what we should do. For most people, their mind's reaction to these feelings is simply to try and exert more and more control over the body, rather in the manner of an overbearing teacher with a class of rebellious kids.

The neck, the junction between the head and the body, becomes the battleground for this conflict. Both the muscles at the back of the neck and the musculature around the sides of the neck develop layer upon layer of holding patterns. Our necks become tense and rigid as our minds maintain their ongoing struggle to hold everything down.

Our throat too suffers, though this has been going on for much longer. Generation upon generation of young children in the West has had the right to voice an opinion suppressed. We have had so little experience of speaking our truth that most people don't really know what they do want. They simply react to any perceived sense of control or authority, either in compliance or rebellion.

Childhood and societal conditioning have suppressed our natural expressiveness to an absolutely chronic degree. In my opinion, our fear to express freely is actually the biggest problem that Western society faces. People cling to the power of the group, whether to maintain cultural values, or to oppose them, and simply assume that they do not themselves have power. Actually, we have immense power. But simply believing that is not enough. We have to remove the physical holding at the throat that is the result of generations of suppression.

This chapter will contain several exercises that specifically work these areas. There will be more in the next chapter as well, because exercises for the jaw usually work at the throat level too.

12.1 Thoracic Opening Exercise

This exercise was made famous by YouTube strongman, Elliott Hulse. It requires a Bioenergetic Stool or something similar that you can lean over backwards. See the Lean Over exercise (Chapter 10.1) for more information about this.

IMPORTANT - Because this exercise begins to open both the throat and the mid-back, parts of our body that are invariably quite blocked, be aware that it can prove very intense. Remember not to overdo it, and don't feel bad if it is too much for you at first. See also the warnings in Chapter 10 about over-straining your back prior to trying the exercise.

Equipment: You will need a suitable sofa or similar, as in 10.1.

Timing & Repetitions: I recommend that you start this exercise with a 30-second ding and work up gradually as you feel more confident with it. You may go right up to a 5-minute ding, though most people will find that doing more repetitions, rather than increasing the time length, will provide better results. I generally recommend 3 repetitions.

Warm Up, Rest Position and Closing: It's good to be at least slightly warmed up before beginning this exercise. It is important to use a Rest Position between reps. The Rest Position has two elements. Firstly, come into a simple squat, done without moving your feet from the stretch and with your back upright. Stay in this position for one ding. Then move into the Arch position (4.1) for one ding. To close, simply follow the same sequence.

Method:

☛ With your back to the sofa or Bioenergetic Stool, put your hands along its spine and gradually lower yourself down, exactly as in 10.1. Ensure that the ridge of the sofa is located immediately beneath where your shoulder blades end. This is important because if you balance your weight lower down your back, you may pull muscles in your lower back. If desired, with practice, you may lower the balance point - but in this specific exercise this is not especially useful.

- Once you're in position, if you wish you can allow your arms to reach out above your head, to deepen the stretch still further.
- As soon as you are settled in the position, open your mouth as wide as you can and begin to make a deep hissing sound from your throat. Keep your mouth stretched as wide open as you can throughout. At times there may be an urge to close the mouth a little, but do your best to resist this and to keep stretching. You may notice at some point that an area of holding around the throat or neck releases.
- Remain in this posture with your mouth stretched fully open for one ding.
- When you hear the ding, slowly close your mouth, bring your arms back to your sides, and use them to slowly bring yourself down into a crouch to rest for one ding. Then move for one ding into the Arch pose, 4.1.
- Repeat this sequence 3 times.
- To close, simply spend one ding in the crouch and one in the Arch 4.1.

12.2 Neck Stretch

This exercise makes use of the Bioenergetic principle of stretching a muscle with awareness. If you have a history of neck issues, then consult a doctor before trying this stretch.

Timing & Repetitions: Start with 20 seconds and work up to one minute. Three repetitions is great, though you can also simply do this exercise once to loosen your neck.

Warm Up, Rest Position & Closing: There's no need to be warmed up. In between stretches, simply sit for one ding with your head upright, arms back by your side and feel. To close, do the same for one ding.

Method:

☛ Sit down comfortably, either on the floor or on a chair. Now, reach up with your arms, interlink your fingers and place your hands on the back of your head with your elbows to the front.

☛ Now, gently pull your head down as far as it will go. Don't pull too hard - rather maintain a gentle, sustained pressure. Although your throat will likely be compressed, it should still be possible to breathe through the mouth. Keep your awareness on your neck area and really feel into the muscles there.

☛ Remain in this posture for one ding.

☛ When the ding sounds, gently let go of your neck and slowly bring your head back upright. Remain breathing and feeling your neck for one ding.

☛ Repeat 3 times.

12.3 Gentle Neck Release

This relaxing exercise is great after a day's work, especially if you have been on the computer a lot. Once again, if you have a history of neck issues, do make sure you check in with a doctor first.

Equipment: You will need a reasonably firm rolled-up yoga mat to use as a bolster.

Timing & Repetitions: Start with a 2-minute ding and work up to 10 minutes. There's no need for reps.

Warm Up, Rest Position & Closing: There's no need for any warm-up or Rest Position with this exercise. To close, simply remove the bolster, lie back and relax for at least one ding.

Method:

- 👉 Lie down on your back on a carpeted floor or yoga mat. Have your legs stretched out and arms relaxed by your sides, palms facing up. Place the bolster, a rolled-up yoga mat, underneath your neck, in such a position that your whole neck is in contact with it.
- 👉 Now, close your eyes, relax and stay focussed on your body as you gently breathe in and out through the mouth. With each out-breath, have the intention to surrender your head and neck a little more. Continue for one ding.
- 👉 When the ding sounds, gently lift your head, remove the bolster and lie back down again, relaxing totally for one ding.

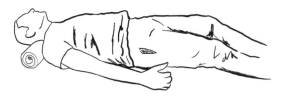

12.4 Deep Neck Release

This sequence of four neck stretches is a great way to mobilise repressed feelings. If you have a history of neck issues, it's important to check with a doctor before giving it a try.

Environment: It's good to make a sound as you come out of each of these stretches. So, do them in an environment where this is okay.

Timing & Repetitions: Do each exercise for around 5 to 10 seconds and then let go. Aim to do them totally and you will not need to increase the length of time or add reps.

Warm Up, Rest Position & Closing: It's important to have your body a little warmed up before beginning. In between each stretch simply keep your head upright, breathe and feel. At the end of the sequence give yourself a few minutes to relax sitting down, feeling your body.

Method:

- Stand upright with your feet firm on the floor, about shoulder-width apart, and with a slight bend in your knees. Breathe through your relaxed mouth and feel your body. Come back to this position for one ding after each stretch.

- **Stretch 1:** Place the palms of your hands on your temples and push your head back. Your elbows should be to the front rather than to the side. Ensure that your head doesn't actually move by tensing your

Stretch 1

neck muscles to resist the movement. Push as hard as you feel comfortable to do and create equal tension in your neck muscles to prevent movement. So, to be clear, there is no actual movement in this exercise - we simply create pressure and resistance in the muscles of our neck.

- When the ding sounds, let your hands go with as loud and expressive a sound as you feel comfortable to make. Actually throw your hands down as you make the sound, as though you were throwing something old out of your very being. Then remain standing and relaxed until the next ding.

👉 **Stretch 2:** Take your left hand and place it on the left side of your head, with the base of your palm pushing to the right, just to the front of your ear. Don't put pressure on your actual ear. Have your elbow to the side.

Stretch 2

👉 Now, push your head to the right and, like before, tense your neck muscles to prevent your head from actually moving. Maintain the pressure and the resistance until the ding.

👉 As before, when the ding sounds, release your hand and throw both hands down with a loud sound of release. As before, remain standing for one ding.

👉 **Stretch 3:** Now take your right hand and place it on the right side of your head, the base of the palm just forwards of the ear once again. Push to the left this time, and once again, with your neck resist moving. Maintain the pressure for one ding.

Stretch 3

👉 When the ding sounds, release as before.

👉 **Stretch 4:** This is the big one. Take both hands and interlink your fingers. Now, placing them right at the back of your head, with your elbows to the front, begin to pull your head forwards and, once again, tense your neck muscles

Stretch 4

to resist. Pull as hard as you feel confident. Remember, there's no actual movement because you also tense your neck muscles equally strongly to resist. Maintain the pressure for one ding.

☛ Release in the same way, throwing both of your hands down with a loud sound.

☛ To complete, sit down comfortably, close your eyes and focus on the natural movements of your belly while you breathe. Do this for at least 3 minutes.

12.5 Gag Reflex Throat Release

This exercise is likely one of the most powerful throat releases around. It can really support you to clear energetic blockages from your throat area. However, gagging is somewhat taboo in Western culture, and so not everyone feels comfortable doing it. In addition, there are some clinical concerns which apply to those from certain backgrounds.

It is not necessary to actually vomit when performing the Gag Reflex, merely to activate the reflex.

Important: If you have a history of eating disorders or any condition where you would make yourself vomit, then you need to check in with a suitably qualified doctor or psychologist prior to doing this exercise.

Equipment: It's good to do this exercise near a sink, or have a spit bowl handy. Have paper tissue near to hand too.

Timing & Repetitions: Generally, I find 6 reflexes in a row to be an effective and safe way to begin clearing the throat. I would not recommend doing more than this. I also would not recommend doing the sequence of 6 more than once a day.

Warm Up, Rest Position & Closing: There's no need for a warm-up. I recommend 6 reps, taking maybe 20 seconds to simply stand up in between each one. At the end, it's important to sit or lie down and relax for around 10 minutes.

Method:

- Decide which hand you would prefer to use to stimulate the reflex and give it a thorough clean, especially the first two fingers. Then place the first two fingers down into your throat. Allow them to go as far as you can easily reach.

- Using the pads of your fingertips, begin to make gentle circles on the inside front of your throat. Continue this until you succeed in stimulating the reflex. Remove your hand and allow the reflex to complete. You do not need to continue the stimulation for so long that you actually vomit, just enough to stimulate the reflex.
- Once the reflex has completed, stand for around 20 seconds. Then begin again and stimulate another gag reflex, until you have completed 6.
- To close, simply sit or lie down and relax, continuing, of course to feel your body and breathing however feels natural to you. Do this for at least 5 minutes.

12.6 Growling Release

Developing your ability to growl like an animal can create powerful energetic effects. As we shall see again, when we get to the chapter on Primal exercises, many simple things that animals do serve to keep them healthy and strong. Be proud to be a primate!

Likely the most useful thing that learning to growl can give you is the reopening of the channel between the belly and the throat. There is a natural connection between these areas of the body early in life, but we learn to shut it down as our parents or society induce in us a fear of natural expression. It is this channel that, when open, most puts us in our power in life. It gives us the ability to simply speak our truth and to hold our ground.

Timing & Repetitions: Start with 1 minute and work up to 5 or 10. There's no need for repetitions.

Warm Up, Rest Position & Closing: There's no need to be warmed up or to use a Rest Position. To close, simply stand or sit down, breathing and feeling into your body.

Method:
- Stand upright with your legs about shoulder-width apart and your knees slightly bent. Have your eyes open, breathe through your mouth and relax your lower jaw. Have your arms relaxed and hanging by your side.
- Now, begin making the lowest sound you can in your throat and add a vibration to it, such that it sounds like an animal growl. While you make the sound, feel into your belly area. Continue for one ding.

- At the ding, simply remain standing with your knees bent. Breathe and feel into your body for one ding. Alternatively, you may sit down and do the same if you wish.
- To close, you can either remain standing or sit or lie down. Breathe and feel your body.

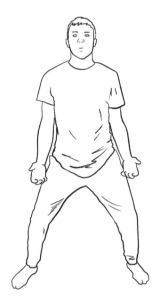

The Face, Eyes & Head

With the head, we complete our tour of our body. It's been quite a journey. And it's by no means over yet! One of the exciting things about our head, and our face in particular, is that the tensions we hold here affect a lot of other areas of our body. This is because, for most of us, we are very concerned with our facial expression. Our face is where we meet the world, and most of us have been socially conditioned into trying to maintain a happy face, regardless of what we're actually feeling inside. Over time, this creates quite a tension in the face. And because we are maintaining this false, happy look by repressing feelings into many areas of our muscle system so, as we work on the face, these areas can release too. This is exciting news!

13.1 Fake Smile Exercise

The smile is actually a very powerful gesture. When we lift the corners of our mouth, we open an energetic circuit in our heart centre, in the middle of our chest. It relaxes us and creates a good feeling. This is very likely why smiling is such a universally accepted symbol of goodwill and contentment.

In the ancient Chinese Daoist tradition, smiling was practised as a meditation, either with a gentle smile on the lips, or simply imagining it inside. This latter version was known as the Inner Smile. With the Bioenergetic version, we make it more of a physical exercise.

Timing & Repetitions: Start with 2 minutes and work up to 10 minutes. Repetitions are not usually done, but feel free to experiment here.

Warm Up, Rest Position & Closing: No warm-up or Rest Position is necessary. If you are trying reps, then simply walk around for a little in between stages. A good way to close is to allow your body to shake for 5 minutes (5.4).

Method:

- Walk slowly around the room, breathing through the mouth and keeping your awareness in your body, feeling.
- Now, raise the corners of your mouth, creating a big smile. Don't worry about whether you feel like smiling or not. It is just an exercise. Keep the corners of your mouth up, as high as they will go, compressing the cheek muscles.

Maintain the stretch, still slowly walking around, and breathing through the mouth until you hear the ding. (Note, you will need to keep your mouth slightly open so that you can breathe through it).
- Remember, for this exercise to really create a release, you will have to fake smile to the absolute max and not let up until the

ding. Perhaps, you could imagine you're working the front desk of a corporate hotel chain, and you have to smile all day, or else you'll get the sack!

☛ If you wish to do reps, you can go back to walking, without the smile, for one ding, then return to the Fake Smile.

☛ To close, stand, put your feet about shoulder-width apart, and begin to shake (5.4). Keep breathing deep and really keep your awareness in your body, feeling everything that's going on. Continue shaking for 2 dings.

13.2 Jaw Stretch

This simple stretch opens up the jaw and is also great for releasing holding patterns from the throat and neck. I consider it a very important exercise.

Like the Fake Smile (13.1), this exercise is usually fairly easy to begin with. But if you want to get a real release, you will need to maintain the stretch fully until the ding. Dropping it for a few seconds when it gets intense will not give you much.

Timing & Repetitions: Start with 1 minute and work up to 5 minutes. Doing repetitions may well increase the release. You can try them and see how it is for you.

Warm Up, Rest Position & Closing: No warm-up is required. If you are doing reps, then simply stand with your jaw relaxed for one ding between each one. To close, I recommend starting with some shaking and then sit down and relax.

Method:

- Stand upright in a grounded position, with your feet about shoulder-width apart and your knees slightly bent.

- Now, open your mouth as wide as you possibly can and keep it stretched open wide. You need to maintain the stretch, always trying to open it a little more. Perhaps imagine you are a teenager, eating your first triple cheeseburger, and you're determined to get it into your mouth whole. (Or a triple veggie burger if you prefer!). Continue to breathe through the mouth. If you make an aspirated hissing sound on the out-breath, this will support the release from the throat. Maintain the stretch for one ding.

- If you're doing 3 reps, then between each one simply stand with your jaw relaxed, breathing gently through the mouth and feeling your body. Do this for one ding.

- This can be a powerful exercise. So, when it comes to closing, make sure you allocate the same amount of time as for the exercise. You can stand and shake, or sit down and tune in to the movements of your belly as you breathe naturally.

13.3 Wide Mouth Bow

This is an excellent variation on the Jaw Stretch (13.2) which increases the degree of opening, as well as activating other muscle systems in the body.

Timing and Repetitions: Start with 1 minute and work up to 5 minutes. Doing repetitions is great with the Wide Mouth Bow. I recommend 3 reps, though if you're really getting into it, you can increase that up to 6.

Warm Up, Rest Position & Closing: There's no need for a warm-up. Use the Arch Exercise (4.1) as a Rest Position between reps. Do it for one ding. The Wide Mouth Bow can be a powerful exercise, so make sure you take at least 5 dings of rest afterwards. This could be shaking, or sitting and simply feeling the natural movements of the belly.

Method:

☞ Stand in the Bow position (4.2). Your arms should be above your head, parallel and with palms facing front, and also stretching back behind the ears. Your pelvis is pushed forwards and you stick your chest out. Your neck, however, is upright and your eyes are open, looking straight ahead. Breathe in and out through your mouth and keep feeling into your body.

☞ Now, while maintaining the Bow position, open your mouth as wide as you can, exactly as in 13.2. Keep it stretched wide open for one ding.

☞ At the ding, gently bring your arms down, straighten your body and allow your jaw to relax. Now, beginning the movement with your head, slowly lean forwards until you are in the Arch position (4.1).

☞ Complete 3 reps and then take at least 5 minutes of rest. You can allow your body to shake, or you can just sit or lie down.

13.4 Jaw Stretch with Eyes Wide Open

This variation on the Jaw Stretch (13.2) creates an additional release by also stretching the eyes wide open.

Having our eyes open wide is a gesture associated with shock. Cartoons depicting a car crash or similar invariably show figures with eyes wide open. The brain opens the eyes wide in dangerous situations to try and gather as much visual information as possible about what's happening. We can make use of this to also release shock from the body.

By opening our eyes as wide as we can, while breathing deeply through the mouth, any sense of shock held within starts to come to the surface and can be released.

Important: This can be a very powerful release. If you feel that a lot is getting stirred up, then don't overdo it at first. Use a short ding time and low number of reps. Remember, little and often releases far more in the long run.

Timing & Repetitions: Start with 30 seconds and work up to 3 minutes. Doing repetitions will increase the release but is not strictly necessary. If you wish to do reps, then 3 is great. If desired, you can increase the number of reps up to 6.

Warm Up, Rest Position & Closing: No warm up is needed. If you're doing reps then simply stand, with your knees unlocked and your heels on the floor, for one ding in between rounds. To close, you can shake for a few minutes and then sit down and stay present in your body for another few minutes.

Method:

☛ As in 13.2, stand upright in a grounded position, with your feet about shoulder-width apart and your knees very slightly bent.

☛ Now, open your mouth and your eyes as wide as you possibly can and keep both stretched open wide. Continue to breathe through the mouth. If you make an aspirated hissing sound on the out-breath, this will support the release from the throat. Maintain the stretch for one ding.

☛ If you're doing 3 reps, then between each one simply stand with your jaw relaxed, breathing gently through the mouth and feeling your body. Do this for one ding.

☛ This can be a powerful exercise. So, when it comes to closing, make sure you allocate the same amount of time as you had for the exercise, especially if this is one of the first times you've done this stretch. You can stand and shake, or sit down and tune into the movements of your belly as you breathe naturally.

☛ Note: This exercise, like 13.2, can also be performed in the Bow Position (4.2)

13.5 Dragon's Breath

This famous exercise has been a stalwart of Body-based Therapy for decades and, like many of the older Bioenergetics exercises, no one really knows for sure where it comes from. It's my pleasure to reproduce it here, to help assist its continuation into the next generations. The Dragon's Breath can also be an excellent warm-up exercise to get you fired up before an emotional expression session or similar.

Timing & Repetitions: Start with 30 seconds and work up to two minutes. It's actually more about how much effort you put into it rather than how long you do it for. There's no need for reps as you do the release on the out-breath and return to the starting position for the in-breath.

Warm Up, Rest Position & Closing: There's no need for a warm-up or Rest Position. To close, make sure you have at least 5 minutes downtime, sitting, shaking or lying down.

Method:

☛ Stand upright with your feet wider than shoulder-width apart. The outsides of your feet should be roughly parallel. Bend your knees to bring your ass lower. Keep your backbone upright.

☛ Now, imagine that you are a big, angry dragon. Maybe something has woken you up early and you're really not happy about it.

☛ Imagining your arms are your dragon wings. Bring them forwards.

☛ When ready, perform the following actions simultaneously... lean forwards, extend your neck, bring your arms back, stick your tongue out and hiss from the throat, while your eyes spit fire. Do this for one full out-breath. You may need to practice it a few times to get the feel for it. What's particularly important is that you really extend your neck and stick your tongue out while hissing loud from the throat. This is where the release comes from. At the end of the out-breath, return to the starting position for the in-breath. Repeat until you hear the ding.

☛ Once complete, allow your body to shake for a few minutes, then sit or lie down. You have just completed the Dragon's Breath!

13.6 Gargoyle Release

This exercise is very similar to the last one, Dragon's Breath, but it is usually done sitting. The posture is taken from that of a gargoyle, a type of grotesque mini-statue found on medieval religious buildings to ward off evil. The word "gargoyle" also refers to the throat, and this exercise is excellent for opening the throat up. In addition, it's a great "quick fix" when you've been sitting down working at the computer and you want something to loosen you up. Just make sure your workmates don't see you, unless they're into Bioenergetics!

Timing & Repetitions: Start with 1 minute and work up to 2 or 3 minutes. There's no need for reps as, like Dragon's Breath, while performing the exercise you will anyway come in and out of the release part of the posture.

Warm Up, Rest Position & Closing: There's no need for a warm-up, neither a Rest Position. To close, just spend a few minutes sitting, feeling your body, to integrate the exercise.

Method:
☛ Sit down on a chair with your feet flat on the floor and your eyes open. Alternatively, you may sit on the floor or a cushion. Breathe

in and out through the mouth. Your
hands should be in your lap.

☛ Now, in one movement, extend
your neck, open your eyes as wide
as possible, open your mouth as
wide as possible, stick your tongue
out and down the chin, and hiss
from the throat. Maintain the release for one full out-breath.

☛ At the end of the out-breath, return
to the start position, sitting relaxed,
for one full in-breath. Then repeat
until the ding.

☛ Once complete, sit and relax for a few minutes. Remember, don't
space out! Breathe and feel your body.

☛ **Tip!** Check that your tongue is sticking right out and down your
chin. Often, I see people doing this exercise but their tongue
stays partly in. You don't get so much of a release like that.

13.7 Intensified Gargoyle Release

This exercise is similar to the Gargoyle Release above (13.6). The
difference is that you don't come back to rest on the in-breath, but
rather screw your face up as much as you can. Pull all the muscles
of your face tight on the in-breath and then do the Gargoyle Release
pose on the out-breath. Repeat with the breath until the ding and then
sit relaxed for several minutes to close.

13.8 Jaw Release Sequence

The jaw is an area where you will find high levels of unnecessary tension in most people. We are not covering Reichian Characterology in this book, but people from a "Rigid" background invariably have a large amount of tension in their jaw.

Jaw tension is associated with pride and inflexibility. It's also symptomatic of repressed anger. The exercises we will be using to release that tension, like much of Bioenergetics, function by actually increasing the tension to the point where the muscles start to release naturally.

Equipment: You will need a piece of clean cloth to chew on for the final exercise.

Timing & Repetitions: Start with a 20-second ding and work up to one minute. There's no need to repeat the sequence, but it is fine to add reps if you feel to. 3 reps is great in that case.

Warm Up, Rest Position & Closing: There's no need to warm up first. In between active elements of the sequence, simply allow your face to relax for one ding. To close, remain sitting, breathe and feel your body.

Method:
- Sit down on a chair or a cushion.
- **Jaw Release 1** - Stick your lower jaw out aggressively, like a Pit Bull terrier. Push it out as far as you can and from your throat make a growling sound. Allow your facial expression to radiate aggression. Maintain this stretch and growl for one ding.

- At the ding, allow your face to relax for one ding. Move your jaw around if this feels good.
- **Jaw Release 2** - Do the same as Jaw Release 1 but this time, while growling, also move your lower jaw from side to side. Maintain for one ding, then relax your jaw for one ding.
- **Jaw Release 3** - Repeat Jaw Release 2 but this time with a piece of clean cloth in your mouth to chew on. Maintain for one ding.
- To close, simply relax your face, remain sitting and breathe and feel your body for 5 minutes.

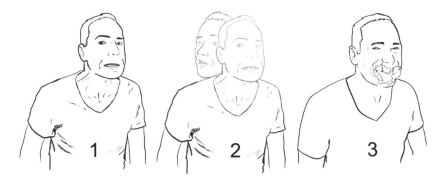

13.9 Masseter Release

The Masseter muscles are located on either side of the face and are the principal muscles we use when chewing food. They run from the lower edge of the cheek-bone down to the jaw. Back in the early days of Body-based Therapy, it was often said that anger was re-pressed into these muscles. I don't know if this is strictly true, but certainly these muscles are often tense and there is a way to release that tension.

Environment: For this exercise, you need to be in a place where you can scream out loud.

Timing & Repetitions: This exercise is usually done once, with intensity, for a period of roughly 10-15 seconds. There is no need for reps.

Warm Up, Rest Position & Closing: It's good to have your body at least slightly warmed up before doing the Masseter Release exercise. You don't do reps so there's no need for a Rest Position. To close, just remain sitting, breathing and feeling your body.

Method:

- With your body at least slightly warmed up, sit down on a chair or the floor.
- Now, locate the Masseter muscle on either the left or right side of your face. The best way to do this is to find the lower edge of your cheek-bone, and then feel about one inch (25 mm) down from here, or about midway to your jawbone below.
  Look in an anatomical textbook, if you're not sure. It is quite a big muscle. It's important, when we start with the exercise, that you are not grinding into the jawbone or cheek-bone.
- Make your right hand into a fist. You will be grinding into the Masseter muscle with the middle set of knuckles. These are the knuckles nearest to the middle of your fingers.
- Place these knuckles onto the muscle, on the right side of the face, in between the jawbone and cheek-bone and grind them around, while keeping your mouth open and allowing sound to come out.
- Start gently and then increase the pressure until you're at the maximum you can bear.

- ☛ **IMPORTANT:** You must keep your mouth open and make some level of sound throughout this exercise. When something gets painful, we often close our throat and shut off making sound. This locks feelings inside and is not healthy in this exercise. So, ensure your mouth is open and that some level of sound is coming out before you begin applying pressure.
- ☛ Continue grinding for one ding. Rest for one ding and then repeat with the other hand and the other side of the face for one ding.
- ☛ Complete by relaxing your jaw, breathing and feeling your body for at least 5 minutes.
- ☛ **Note:** You can also do this exercise with a friend, getting them to sit behind you, supporting your head with one hand and grinding into the masseter with the other. Use hand gestures to ask for more or less pressure.

13.10 Head Drop

This very simple exercise can be useful to relax your neck after working on the computer.

Timing & Repetitions: You won't need dings for this one. 5 reps is good.

Warm Up, Rest Positions & Closing: No opening required. No Rest Position needed. To close, simply sit and feel your body for 2 minutes.

Method:
- ☛ Sit down, either on a chair or a cushion. Have your backbone and head upright, your face looking straight ahead.
- ☛ Close your eyes and allow your head to simply drop, such that your chin travels towards your chest as far as it will naturally go.

Try not to force the head to drop, but rather to allow it to simply fall by relaxing your neck muscles. Stay in your body, feeling what happens as you let go and your head drops. Be fully present with the experience.

- ☛ Ensure that only your head drops. The rest of your body remains relaxed but stationary.
- ☛ After your head has been in this dropped position for about 5 seconds, open your eyes and bring it back up, so that you come back to the starting position.
- ☛ Repeat 5 times and then close by sitting in the starting position and just feeling your body for 2 minutes.

13.11 Head Shake Release

This is another great exercise to help you relax your neck and head after working on the computer. Go easy with it the first few times.

Important: If you have any history of neck issues, then do check in with a medical professional prior to trying this exercise.

Timing & Repetitions: Start with 15 seconds and work up to one minute. Repetitions are not needed but it's also fine to do 3 if desired.

Warm Up, Rest Position, Closing: It's good to be at least slightly warmed up before beginning this exercise. If you're doing reps then just remain sitting and relax for one ding between each repetition. To close, remain seated, eyes closed, breathing through the mouth and feeling inside. Do this for at least 2 minutes.

Method:

☛ Sit down on a cushion or chair. Have your head and backbone upright and close your eyes.

☛ Relax your lower jaw, have your mouth slightly open and your tongue relaxed. Now, gently shake your head from side to side, while breathing deeply through the mouth. Continue for one ding.

☛ Note, you should feel your lower jaw moving slightly independently from the rest of your head. If you don't then open your mouth a little more and try to relax your jaw further. In addition, try to not lock your neck in any way.

☛ If you're doing reps, then rest in the start position for one ding, then continue. To close, simply rest in the start position for a couple of minutes, still breathing through the mouth and feeling your body.

13.12 Eye Stretch Sequence

It has been discovered that simply moving your eyeballs around can release holding patterns, even though very little physical movement takes place. There is even a whole therapy, called Eye Movement Desensitisation & Reprocessing (EMDR), that developed from this principle.

This sequence of four simple eye stretches can be very powerful. It's important to maintain the stretch and to continue breathing through the mouth.

Timing & Repetitions: Start with a 2-minute ding and work up to 7 minutes. Repetitions are not needed

Warm Up, Rest Positions & Closing: It's good to be at least slightly warmed up before commencing this exercise. No Rest Positions are needed. To complete, simply sit with your eyes closed for 10 minutes. Keep feeling your body. Alternately, if you prefer, you may lie down, outstretched and relax for 10 minutes.

Method:

☛ Sit down on a chair or cushion. Have your backbone and head upright, your eyes open facing the front.

☛ **Eye Stretch 1** - Keeping your head facing front, look as far to the left as you possibly can. Keep stretching your gaze to the left for one ding. Do not look anywhere else. You may find this easier to do if you place an object at the extreme left of your gaze. This can be an "anchor" for your gaze. Try not to move your head at all.

☛ **Eye Stretch 2** - When the ding sounds, return your gaze to the front for a few seconds and then look to the far right.

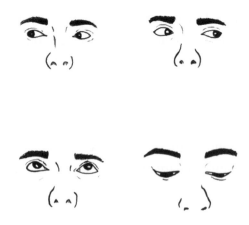

- **Eye Stretch 3** - When the ding sounds, return your gaze once again to the front briefly and then look up, as far as you can without moving your head.
- **Eye Stretch 4** - When the ding sounds, return your gaze to the front and then look as far down as you can.
- At the ding, close the exercise by either lying down, eyes closed and relaxing, or by sitting, eyes closed and relaxing. This can be a powerful exercise, so I recommend you spend at least 10 minutes relaxing before continuing with your day.
- **Note:** What is frequently difficult is to ensure that your head remains facing forwards while your gaze is to the side. In practice, you just have to trust that it is, as if you move your gaze to check you break the stretch.

13.13 Eye Rotation Exercises

Another, equally powerful way that we can use the eyes to release old patterns of holding from the body is by rotating the gaze. Osho Mandala Meditation makes use of this practice in one of its stages. We shall use a similar technique here. This exercise is done lying down.

Equipment: You need somewhere comfortable to lie down for half an hour. It should not be so comfortable that you fall asleep!

Timing & Repetitions: Start with 5 minutes and work up to 15 minutes. Repetitions are not needed.

Warm Up, Rest Position & Closing: Your body should be at least slightly warmed up and you should not be too sleepy. There's no Rest Position. To close the exercise, simply relax back, still lying down, with your eyes closed. Remain like this for at least 10 minutes.

Method:

- Lie down with your arms by your side and legs stretched out lengthwise. Ensure you are not too uncomfortable, but also not so comfortable that you might fall asleep. Have your eyes open and keep them open throughout this exercise. Look straight up at the ceiling.

- Without moving your head, begin to rotate your gaze in one direction, making sweeps that are as wide as possible. You can start slow and, if you feel confident, begin to speed up the rotation. Remember that your head stays relaxed, but it does not move. Only your eyeballs move. You may breathe in through the nose or mouth, whichever feels most comfortable. Breathe out through the mouth. Try to keep feeling your body throughout. Maintain the rotation for one ding.

- When the ding sounds, begin to rotate your eyes in the opposite direction. Once again, start slow and increase the speed of rotation if you feel confident. Maintain for one ding.

- To close this exercise, close your eyes, lie back and relax for at least 10 minutes.

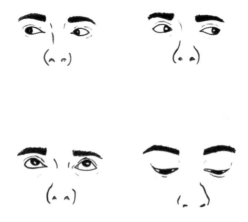

Chapter

14

Whole Body Techniques

Having worked our way through the body, from the feet up, now it's time to look at some Bioenergetic exercises that work the whole body, or more than just one area of it. Remember, though, that just because an exercise focuses on one area of the body doesn't mean that its effects are limited to that area, physically or psychologically. Many of the exercises in this book work in multiple areas of our body and psyche.

Let's look at some of these exercises.

14.1 Sitting Full Body Compression

This is a great exercise that can be done pretty much anywhere, even in your workspace. It only takes a minute and it can help to release tensions that naturally start to accumulate while we work.

Timing & Repetitions: 10 seconds of compression and 10 seconds of relaxation is great. It's not necessary to increase this, as you become more experienced. It's better to instead increase the intensity with which you do the exercise. Three repetitions is a good amount.

Warm Up, Rest Positions & Closing: No warm-up is needed. Take 10 seconds of rest, just sitting, after each 10 seconds of release. To close, simply return to sitting, breathing and feeling your body.

Method:

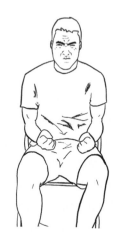

- ☞ Sit down on a chair or on the floor and spend a few seconds really breathing and feeling your body. If you're in a chair, make sure that your feet are firm on the floor.
- ☞ Now, as you breathe in through the mouth, tense every muscle you can access in your body, from the tips of your toes to the top of your head. Include especially your face. Pull every muscle tight and hold that posture for 10 seconds.
- ☞ Note: With some body areas - eyes, mouth, hands, etc - you will need to choose which way to tighten them, there being at least two options. You may wish to tighten those muscles one way in one rep, and another way in the next rep.
- ☞ After 10 seconds, breathe out and relax, consciously trying to let go and to feel your body as much as you can. Do this for 10 seconds.
- ☞ Complete 3 repetitions.
- ☞ To close, simply remain relaxed for one or two minutes, breathing and really feeling your body.

14.2 Dog-Lion Release

This is a great release and also an excellent way to integrate the upper and lower halves of the body. Although the Dog posture is commonly found in Yoga, which you may be familiar with, please ensure you do it the "Bioenergetic way," as described below.

Equipment: If your floor or carpet is a little slippery, then make use of a yoga mat for this exercise.

Timing & Repetitions: Start with 10 seconds and work up to 1 minute. Complete 3 repetitions. You can increase the number of reps up to 6 if you feel confident.

Warm Up, Rest Position & Closing: You don't need any warm-up for this exercise, nor a Rest Position. To close, come into Child Pose (5.5).

Method:
☛ Note that in this pair of postures only your palms, your toes and the balls of your feet should be in contact with the floor. The rest of your body stays off the floor throughout. Your fingers should point forwards.
☛ This exercise starts with the Dog pose, which is similar to the Down-facing Dog posture commonly found in Yoga. Have only your palms and the toes and balls of your feet on the floor. Straighten your arms and legs fully. Your heels should not touch the floor, so that on the out-breath you can press them towards the floor, stretching the backs of the legs. Dipping your chest a little can help to open up the shoulder blades more. Have your neck relaxed and your head simply hanging.

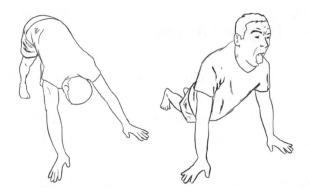

☛ Remain in this posture, with your arms and legs fully stretched until the ding. Keep pressing your heels towards the floor, especially on the out-breath.

☛ When the ding sounds, come into the Lion pose. You drop your crotch, keeping it off the floor, and raise your upper body. You keep your palms and toes on the floor - they do not move from where they were in the Dog pose. Lean slightly forwards on your hands. Open your eyes and mouth wide, stick your tongue out and roar from the throat. Look aggressive. Hold this pose, roaring like a lion, until the ding and then return to the Dog pose.

☛ Complete 3 reps without any Rest Position. To close, come into Child Pose (5.5) with knees wide. Remain like this, breathing and feeling, for 3 dings.

14.3 Cat-Cow Release

This pair of postures are also similar to those found in Yoga. Remember, though, that this is Bioenergetics and the focus is subtly different from Yoga.

Psychologically, the Cat posture, with your back pressing up and your head bowed down, represents oppression - the feeling that someone is controlling you and there's nothing you can do about it. When you come out into the Cow posture, with your back down and your head up, you roar freedom!

Timing & Repetitions: A 15 or 20-second ding is good for this pair of postures. You actually don't need to increase this - it's better to put more energy into each position, as you become confident. 3 repetitions are good.

Warm Up, Rest Position & Closing: You don't need to be warmed up, nor is there a Rest Position. To close, as in 14.2, simply come into Child Pose (5.5).

Method:

☞ Come into the "tabletop" position, with both palms on the floor facing forwards. Your hands should be under your shoulders and with a small amount of flex at the elbows. Your knees and feet are on the floor, with your knees directly under your hips and your toes pointing backwards, or tucked as you prefer.

☞ Now, move your body into the Cat pose. Arch your back upwards as much as you can. Simultaneously, bring your head down, pulling it towards your crotch. Have the feeling of being oppressed,

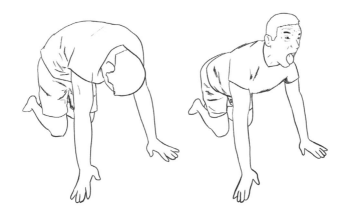

of being told what to do. Continue to stretch into this pose for one ding.

- ☞ With the ding, move quickly into the Cow pose. Bring your back down, as far as you can and, simultaneously, raise your head right up. Lean forwards on your hands, stick your tongue out and down, and roar. Roar for your freedom. Show the world that you're not going to take being oppressed any longer. Maintain this for one ding.
- ☞ Complete 3 reps.
- ☞ To close, bring your ass back towards your heels and come into Child Pose, 5.5, with your knees wide and your feet close together.

14.4 Tantrum

The final three exercises in this chapter introduce some emotional expression elements to your practice of Bioenergetics. They have been favourites of therapists working in this field for decades. These exercises will need to be done in an environment where you can make shouting and screaming noises.

The tantrum exercise is drawn from infant psychology. When little kids don't get what they want, often they will throw a tantrum. They lie down, move their body around, and scream. While this can be pretty annoying for people around them, it does serve to allow some natural release for them from the feeling inside. As we grow up, we learn not to release. And, while a part of this is simply becoming more adult and learning to accept the unfairness of life, there is another part where it is healthy to give expression to the feeling inside. This also helps us move on.

This exercise is drawn from the classic infant tantrum that you will see many small children regularly throwing. It is important that you include each element of this Tantrum exercise.

Equipment: You will need a mat or similar surface to lie on. It should be sufficiently firm that you can bash it with your fists without hurting yourself.

Environment: It's important to make sound in this exercise, so ensure you're in a place where you can scream and shout.

Music: If you wish you can play some loud, aggressive music in the background to support the release.

Timing & Repetitions: With this exercise, it's best not to use a ding track, but rather to continue until you are simply exhausted. For most people, this takes around 20-30 seconds. There's no need to do repetitions.

Warm Up, Rest Position & Closing: It's good to warm your body up before you start the Tantrum exercise. There's no Rest Position. To close, simply lie back on the floor in 5.3. As usual, breathe through the mouth and feel your body. Remain like this for at least 3 minutes.

Method:
☛ Lie back on the mat in the Classic Leg Rest pose, 5.1.
☛ When you feel ready, begin these three bodily movements in sequence:
  ☞ Kick your heels down into the mat, one after the other
  ☞ Maintaining the kicking, make fists and begin to pound them down into the mat, one after the other.

☞ Finally, maintaining the other two, move your head from side to side, as though looking from the left to the right.

☛ While doing these three movements, you must also make sound. This is very important. Open your mouth and scream and shout.

☛ Continue these three movements, with constant screaming, until you feel exhausted. In fact, do them so intensely that you try to exhaust yourself. This may well take only 15 or 20 seconds and this is fine. If you're still going at around one minute, then you can anyway come to a stop.

☛ To close, lie back on the mat with your limbs stretched out (5.3). Continue to breathe through your mouth and stay present in your body, feeling what's going on. Remain like this for at least 3 minutes. If you wish, after a couple of minutes, you can roll over onto your side and get into the fetal position.

14.5 Pillow Bashing

This exercise will support you to hold better boundaries for yourself. It's important to do it in an environment where you can shout and make noise. It's one of those classic therapeutic exercises that certain comedians love to make fun of, but it actually can provide a deep level of release. It can be done as a stand-alone practice, or as the conclusion of other Bioenergetics exercises, such as the Shoulder Opening Sequence, 11.1 - 11.4, or the Teenager Release, 11.5.

Important: As this exercise has a large element of emotional expression in it, be aware that it can bring up a lot of feelings afterwards. If you are new to it, then give yourself space to relax and integrate upon completion. In addition, if you do have any history of psychiatric issues or are on mood-altering medication, then do check in first with a suitably qualified clinician - to see if it is a safe practice for you to try. Take responsibility.

Equipment: You will need one good solid cushion that won't easily burst open. It also needs to be firm enough that you can bring both fists down on it hard without hurting yourself in any way. My preferred cushions for this exercise are moon-shaped Zafu cushions, filled with buckwheat hulls and stitched strongly together. You can find them online easily if you don't have a Yoga store nearby.

Environment: It's important to make sound in this exercise, so ensure you're in a place where you can scream and shout.

Music: Although not strictly necessary, playing some loud, aggressive music in the background can support you to release, as well as reduce any self-consciousness that you might feel about shouting.

Timing & Repetitions: As in the Tantrum exercise (14.4) above, it's good to try and exhaust yourself with this exercise if you can. This exercise is slightly less physical than 14.4, so don't worry if you don't get exhausted through doing it. Simply be as intense as you can for 1 minute and then bring it to a close. No repetitions are needed.

Warm Up, Rest Position & Closing: It's important to have your body warmed up before you start. There's no Rest Position. To close, come into the Child Pose, 5.5, and remain there for a few minutes, breathing through the mouth and feeling your body. If a lot has been stirred up, then also spend time simply lying on your back, with your limbs outstretched, relaxed. As always, try to stay in your body, feeling what's going on. Remember, the simple act of feeling the body creates integration.

Method:

☛ Kneel on the floor, or a mat, with the cushion in front of you.

☛ Now, make two fists, with your thumbs on the outside, and place them next to each other. It's important to not interlock your fingers, or you may hurt yourself when you bring your hands down.

☛ Come up on your knees, so your upper legs are vertical.

☛ Raise your fists, keeping them side-by-side, and stretch back as far as you can. It's important to stretch right back as this increases the release.

☛ Now, bring your fists down hard onto the cushion. Shout the word "No!" as powerfully as you can as you hit the cushion. Try to involve your belly in the sound.

☛ Repeat and continue at your own speed, but not taking too long between strikes. Remember to not interlock your fingers and to stretch right back with your arms each time you go up.

☛ Continue until you feel exhausted or the ding sounds.

☛ To close, push the cushion out of the way and lean forwards into the Child Pose, 5.5. Stay in this posture, breathing through the mouth and feeling your body, for several minutes. If you're aware that a lot is still going on inside, then, after this, lie down on your back, relaxing with your limbs outstretched.

Note: Be aware, when working with anger in this way, that it is quite normal to feel vulnerable or tearful afterwards. Allow this.

14.6 Towel Whacking Release Exercise

This is another, classic exercise from the old days of Body-based Therapy. Sometime last century, someone noticed that whacking a knotted-up towel on the floor gave a curiously satisfying release! This exercise has been popular in therapy groups ever since.

Equipment: You will need an old towel with a knot tied in one end of it. Generally, a fairly long and lightweight towel is easiest to use. This exercise is best done on a fairly solid floor, perhaps a wooden one.

Environment: It's good to make sound in this exercise. Ensure you're in a place where you can at least grunt loudly and where the sound of the towel hitting the floor will not disturb others.

Timing & Repetitions: Like the previous two exercises, it's good to do this exercise until you feel that any internal pressure or anxiety has drained away. 30 seconds to a minute should be adequate. There's no need for repetitions.

Warm Up, Rest Position & Closing: It's good to be at least slightly warmed up before beginning this exercise. No Rest Position is required. To close, simply sit or lie down, breathe through the mouth and remain feeling your body for 2 minutes.

Method:

- ☛ Stand up with the towel in your right hand (left hand if you're left-handed). Hold it by the end that isn't knotted.
- ☛ When you're ready, swing the knotted end up above your head and bring it down hard, making a grunt sound as it hits the floor.
- ☛ Continue, at your own pace, until you feel you have had a release, or use a 30-second ding.
- ☛ When complete, sit or lie down and put the towel to one side. Breathe and feel your body for a couple of minutes. You may have your eyes open or closed.

Primal Activation Exercises

In this chapter, we shall be looking at a different area of Bioenergetics. Many of the postures we've been doing so far are aimed at working certain muscle groups to allow any charge held there to start to be mobilised and released. Others are working in somatic centres of the body - the belly, the throat, the heart centre - to create some opening where we have shut ourselves down. Still more are working to open up the primary Grounding circuit in the body - from the belly, down through the pelvis and legs, to the soles of our feet. But there is more!

Our body is the product of a billion years of evolution. As such, it is a veritable treasure house of old reflexes and responses, some of which may have served our forebears well, but have now fallen out of use. This chapter will look at a few exercises which make use of these principles. I call them Primal Activation Exercises.

15.1 The Sucking Reflex

The instinct to suck is activated from our DNA when we are born. Similarly, our instinct to breathe, urinate and defecate begin at the same time. But whereas these other instincts continue for as long as we live, the instinct to suck at the mother's breast lasts only for a few years. And, for some of us, we may even never get to fully use it, if, for example we weren't breastfed as babies.

When our instinct to suck is blocked, during our early years, our ability to nourish ourselves throughout our lives is deeply affected, and not just physically. Our capacity to feel good about ourselves, to receive wealth, to go for what we want are all impaired. Performing Bioenergetic sucking exercises can support your brain to "reprogram" itself at a deep level to allow in what nourishes you.

In addition, because we only suck at the breast in early infancy, and then stop, performing these sucking exercises helps to take your brain back to that age. Traumatic events that happened later down the line, and disconnections you've experienced, can come to the surface. There they can be felt and thus find resolution.

We will look at the basic Bioenergetics sucking exercise, and then some variations that work other parts of the body at the same time.

The basic sucking exercise can be done at any time of day. You can even do it in bed, upon waking. It is usually done lying down, though you may also experiment with doing it sitting.

Timing & Repetitions: Start with a 3-minute ding and work up to 60 minutes. There's no need for repetitions.

Warm Up, Rest Position & Closing: You don't need to be warmed up and there is no Rest Position with this exercise. To close, simply stop the sucking movement and stretch out, continuing of course to breathe and to feel your body.

Method:
- 👉 Lie down on a mat or bed. Ensure that you are comfortable. Allow your body to relax.
- 👉 Now, stick your tongue fully out and down your chin. Gently close your lips and suck your tongue back in quickly so that it makes a "tupp" sound. It can take a little while to get the hang of it. Your body will remember just how to do this with a little practice. Don't be discouraged if it doesn't come at once.
- 👉 Continue lying down, performing the sucking movement roughly once every two seconds, until the ding. Keep feeling your body while you do it.
- 👉 Note: This exercise can be more powerful if you do it with eyes open, gently focused on a point on the ceiling. It is also fine to do it with eyes closed, feeling what's going on inside.
- 👉 Also note: Sometimes people report feeling like they "can't breathe" soon after starting this exercise. They start to panic and stop the sucking movement. Actually, you will be able to breathe fine, in and out through the mouth. But this exercise can be so powerful that it brings any form of energetic block in the throat

to the surface. If you feel like you can't breathe while doing it, just persevere gently, making sure that you are allowing air to enter as you open your mouth.

☛ To close, simply stop the sucking movement and relax back, stretching your arms and legs right out. Continue to breathe and feel your body. Do this for at least 10 minutes.

15.2 Three Position Sucking Exercise

Each exercise in this sequence makes use of the sucking gesture, 15.1 above. All three are done lying down. In each exercise, you make the same sucking movement throughout, but alter what you're doing with your lower body.

Timing & Repetitions: Start with a 3-minute ding and, as you get experienced with this sequence, you may increase up to 20 minutes. There's no need for reps.

Warm Up, Rest Position & Closing: You won't need a warm-up or a Rest Position. To close, as in 15.1, simply stop the sucking gesture, stretch out your arms and legs and rest, still feeling your body (5.3). Do this for at least 3 dings.

Method:

☛ **Position 1 - Sucking with Knee Rocking** - Lie on your back on a firm mattress or Yoga mat. Bring your knees up towards your chest, such that your lower legs are roughly horizontal. Gently clasp your legs below the knees. Close your eyes, breathe through your mouth, relax and feel your body.

☛ Now, begin the sucking gesture, 15.1, roughly one time every 2 seconds. At the same time, rock your knees gently towards your chest and away. As your knees gently rock forwards, you suck your tongue in. As your knees rock back down, again suck your tongue in. Continue for one ding, really feeling your pelvic area as you continue these movements.

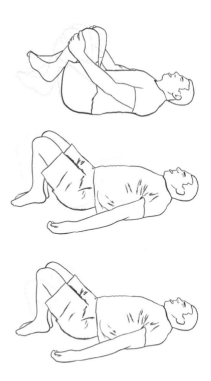

- **Position 2 - Sucking with Pelvic Rotation** - When the ding sounds, continue sucking but bring the soles of your feet to the floor (5.1). Now, as you suck in, rotate your pelvis gently down. As you suck in the next time, rotate your pelvis back up. This pelvic rotation is exactly as in 8.1, so I won't describe it more here. Ensure that you really stay present in your body, feeling throughout. Continue for one ding.

- **Position 3 - Sucking with Knees Flicking Outwards** - When the ding sounds, continue sucking but cease the pelvic rotation movements. Keeping the soles of your feet on the floor, bring them together so that they are gently touching. With each sucking gesture, as your tongue comes in, flick your knees gently outwards and allow them to come back together. In this exercise, you do one flick of the knees outwards each time your tongue sucks in. Remember to stay really present in your body, feeling what's going on. Continue for one ding.

- When the ding sounds, you close the sequence by stopping the movements and simply stretching your limbs out (5.3). Breathe gently through the mouth, keep paying attention to any feelings in your body, lie back and relax. Remain lying down like this for at least 3 dings.

- ☛ Note: This can be an intense process that can bring up a lot of feelings that have been stuck in your body from early infancy, or even before. Do give yourself any downtime you need to integrate before going back to your daily life.
- ☛ Also note: If you wish you can add contracting your anus to any or all of the above exercises. This will increase the degree of primal activation. As you suck your tongue in, you contract your anus. As you bring your tongue back out, you relax your anus.

15.3 Bear Crawl

This simple exercise, found in many bodywork traditions, can really support you to develop your core, both physically and energetically. Bears, like many other mammals, have a natural way of moving that constantly strengthens their physical and energetic core in their belly. Aside from developing your core, on a physical and psychological level, it also increases integration between the upper and lower halves of your body.

Environment: You need a relatively clean, non-slippery floor surface.

Timing & Repetitions: Start with 30 seconds and work up to 5 minutes. There's no need to do reps, but it is fine to do 3 or more reps if you wish. You can use the Dog (14.2) or the Arch pose (4.1) as a Rest Position between reps.

Warm Up, Rest Position & Closing: No warm-up is required. If you are doing reps, then you can use either the Dog pose or the

Arch pose as Rest Positions. The former will intensify the workout as it keeps you on your toes and palms. To close, come into Child Pose, 5.5.

Method:

- Begin in the Dog posture (see 14.2). Your palms and toes should be at least 3 feet (1 metre) apart.
- Now, lift simultaneously one hand and the opposite foot and move forwards, placing both back down on the floor at the same time. Next, do the same with the other hand and foot. Continue moving forward in this way.
- After a while, move backwards in the same way, always moving one hand and the opposite foot at the same time.
- Note: Keep your feet and hands well apart. For most people, this means they don't get closer than 2 feet (60cm) throughout. This is not monkey crawl!
- Note also: It may well take a little while to get used to this way of moving around on all fours. Take your time, and keep checking you've got it right. You won't achieve much unless you get the movement correct.
- Continue until the ding and then close the position by coming into Child Pose, 5.5.

15.4 The Right to Exist Exercise

This exercise, like the sucking exercise, makes use of a primal gesture to create deep change. Like the sucking exercise, it works deep underneath the conscious mind.

In today's world, there are a lot of people who feel, deep inside, that they don't really have the right to be, that they aren't really allowed to do their thing in life and to get their needs met. They may also believe that they don't have the right to hold safe boundaries.

The bottom line is that they don't feel or believe that they have the right to assert themselves in life. This usually comes from the conditions of their early childhood. The Right to Exist exercise starts to reprogram that negative belief at a pre-verbal level. It works simultaneously the belly, pelvis and lower back areas.

Timing & Repetitions: Start with 2 minutes and increase the time as you feel confident. You can go right up to 20 minutes if you wish. There's no need to do reps, but feel free to experiment with reps if you wish. If you do, then you can use the Arch pose (4.1) in between repetitions.

Warm Up, Rest Position & Closing: It's good to at least warm your hips up before starting. Move them around, forwards and backwards and side to side. Ideally, I also recommend that you do the first two stages of the Belly Activation Sequence (9.1) before beginning this exercise. You don't need a Rest Position. To close, it's good to do some shaking (5.4) and then sit or lie down.

Method:

- ☞ Stand with your feet greater than shoulder-width apart and your backbone upright. Your knees should be bent and the outsides of your feet roughly parallel. Have your arms relaxed by your sides, with your arms facing forwards, your palms open as though receiving something.
- ☞ Keeping your knees bent, bring your hips back and then flick them forwards on the out-breath. As you come forwards, expel a deep grunt. The pelvic movement is identical to 8.5 but the sound is deeper. At the same time, allow your face to have an ugly, atavistic look. Stick your lower jaw out and relax your tongue. To increase the effect, also allow your mind to think "I have the right to get what I need" and similar thoughts. Continue until the ding.
- ☞ Note: Ensure that your whole body is not moving backwards and forwards. Your back and lower legs should not be rigid, but they should be relatively static. The movement happens solely in the hips and upper legs.
- ☞ To close, bring your feet together and allow your body to shake for a few minutes, 5.4. Then you may sit or lie down for another 5 - 10 minutes, remembering to keep feeling your body and breathing through the mouth.

Exercises That You Can Do Later in the Day

Something I'm often asked about is whether it's okay to do Bioenergetics in the evening or before you sleep. The answer I've found, over the years, is that for some people this is fine. The exercises seem to support them to get a good night's sleep. For others, however, doing Bioenergetics later in the day gives them too much energy to easily get to sleep. You can try it one time and see which is true for you.

For those of you who would like to have some form of practice to do late in the day, I can recommend the following. Look online for more information.

- Osho Chakra Sounds Meditation
- Osho Nadabrahma Meditation
- Any Vipassana practice where you simply focus on the natural movements of the belly as you breathe.
- Any Body-scan type practice. There are many found in Buddhist meditations, where you are progressively guided through the body, feeling as you go.

Chapter

17

Weekly Exercise Routines

Having worked our way through the body, from the toes all the way to the crown of the head, I will now give you some suggestions on how to create a daily workout for yourself. Remember, by far the best way to make progress is by practising Bioenergetics frequently over a good length of time. It's quite common to get big releases when you start, but you must also be prepared to embark on a slow, steady and thorough journey with Bioenergetics. There are no quick fixes here.

Here's a suggested itinerary for 12 weeks. Each week has a different exercise routine and most last around 30 minutes. You should complete each exercise at least 7 times, on separate days, before moving on to the next.

People are different. Not everyone can proceed at the same speed. So, if you find the suggested weekly workouts below too much for you, then simply reduce the ding times a little and continue.

Remember, the primary mistake most new practitioners of Bioenergetics make is that they over-focus on the posture and under-focus on breathing and feeling. Yes, you need to maintain the posture, but this is only one of the three elements of Bioenergetics. While keeping the posture correct, you must also breathe deeply through the mouth, in and out, and keep feeling your body. For sure, you will forget at times. But, when that happens, just come back to breathing and feeling.

Week 1 - Ankle Stretches plus Bow & Arch

- Ankle Stretches (6.1 - 6.6) for 2 mins each, in sequence, no reps.
- Bow & Arch (4.2 & 4.1) for 90 secs each, 3 reps.
- To Close - Sit down, close your eyes, breathe and feel the natural movements of your belly - 5 mins.
- Workout time - 26 mins.

Week 2 - Leg Stretches plus Bow & Arch

- Leg Stretches (7.1 - 7.4) for 1 min each, 3 reps.
- Bow & Arch (4.2 & 4.1) for 90 secs each, 3 reps.
- To Close: Lie down flat out on your back. Close your eyes, breathe and feel your body - 5 mins.
- Workout time - 26 mins.

Week 3 - Shoulder Stretches plus Bow & Arch

- Shoulder Stretches (11.1 - 11.4) for 3 mins each, no reps.
- Bow & Arch (4.2 & 4.1) for 2 mins each, 3 reps.
- To Close - Sit down, close your eyes, breathe and feel the natural movements of your belly - 5 mins.
- Workout time - 29 mins.

Week 4 - Pelvic Floor Opening plus Bow & Arch

- Pelvic Floor Opening Sequence (8.4), 2 mins each posture, 2 reps.

- Bow & Arch (4.2 & 4.1) for 2 mins each, 3 reps.
- To Close: Lie down flat out on your back. Close your eyes, breathe and feel your body - 5 mins.
- Workout time - 33 minutes.

Week 5 - Belly Activation
- Belly Activation (9.1)
  - 1st Stage - 5 mins;
  - 2nd Stage - 5 mins;
  - 3rd Stage - 10 mins;
- To Close: Sit down, close your eyes, breathe and feel the natural movements of your belly - 5 mins.
- Workout time - 25 mins.

Week 6 - Reverse Prayer & Arm Raise plus Teenager Release
- Reverse Prayer & Arm Raise (11.9); 3 reps of 3 mins.
- Teenager Release (Standing) (11.5); Standing still with your knees slightly bent, lift your shoulders up and then throw them down with a sound of annoyance. After 5 mins, speed up the shoulder movement and make one longer sound. 10 mins total.
- To Close - Sit down, close your eyes, breathe and feel the natural movements of your belly - 5 mins.
- Workout time - 33 mins.

Week 7 - Dog-Lion Release plus Expression Exercises
- Dog-Lion Release (14.2). Use a 30-second ding and alternate between the Dog pose and Lion pose. When doing the Lion, extend your tongue fully out and down and roar, leaning forwards on your hands. 5 mins total.
- Get Off My Back - Elbows (11.6). 1 min.

- Get Off My Back - Legs (7.10). 1 min.
- Pillow Bashing (14.5). 1 min.
- Bow & Arch (4.2 - 4.1). 3 reps, 2 mins.
- To Close: Lie down flat out on your back. Close your eyes, breathe and feel your body - 5 mins.
- Workout time - 26 mins.

Week 8 - Psoas Release

- Psoas Release Sequence (8.7). Set timer to a 2-minute ding and complete the following:
    - DLP Rest Position (5.2) - 2 mins.
    - Psoas Posture 1 (8.7) - 6 mins.
    - DLP Rest Position (5.2) - 2 mins.
    - Psoas Posture 2 (8.7) - 4 mins
    - Psoas Posture 3 (8.7) - 10 mins.
- To Close: Lie down flat out on your back. Close your eyes, breathe and feel your body - 5 mins.
- Workout time - 29 mins.

Week 9 - Bow & Arch

- Bow & Arch (4.2 & 4.1) - 4 reps of 3 mins.
- To Close - Sit down, close your eyes, breathe and feel the natural movements of your belly - 5 mins.
- Workout time - 29 mins.

Week 10 - Right to Exist Exercise

- Belly Activation (9.1)
    - 1st Stage - 3 mins.
    - 2nd Stage - 3 mins.
- Right To Exist Posture (15.5). Pelvic flicks with primal grunt sound, arms with palms facing forwards as though receiving and animal face - 14 mins.

- To Close - Sit down, close your eyes, breathe and feel the natural movements of your belly - 5 mins.
- Workout time - 25 mins.

Week 11 - Three Position Sucking Release
- Sucking Exercise with Knees Rocking (15.2) - 8 mins.
- Sucking Exercise with Pelvic Rotation (15.3) - 8 mins.
- Sucking Exercise with Knees Flicking Outward (15.4) - 8 mins.
- To Close: Lie down flat out on your back. Close your eyes, breathe and feel your body - 5 mins.
- Workout time - 29 mins.

Week 12 - Pelvic Release Sequence
- Pelvic Rotation (8.1) - 8 mins.
- Pelvic Lift & Lower (8.2) - 8 mins.
- Pelvic Bumping (8.3) - 8 mins.
- To Close: Lie down flat out on your back. Close your eyes, breathe and feel your body - 5 mins.
- Workout time - 29 mins.

Resources

1) My website on Bioenergetics, featuring an Online Experiential Bioenergetics Video Course, Follow-along Sessions, Workshops, One-to-one Sessions, Articles and more - **https://www.bioenergetics.org.uk/**

2) Ding Tracks and Grunt Track downloads - **https://bioenergetics.org.uk/Downloads/**

3) Making a Bioenergetic Stool - **https://www.bioenergetics.org.uk/making-a-bioenergetic-stool/**

4) The International Institute for Bioenergetic Analysis - **https://bioenergetic-therapy.com/index.php/en/**

5) Osho Leela, UK - **https://osholeela.uk/**

6) Namaste Centre, Brazil - **https://namaste.com.br**

7) Florida Society for Bioenergetic Analysis - **https://www.bioenergetics-society.com/**

8) Book: The Way to Vibrant Health - Alexander Lowen

9) Book: The 5 Personality Patterns - Stephen Kessler

10) Book: Character Analysis - Wilhelm Reich

11) Book: The Polyvagal Theory: Neurophysiological Foundations of Emotions, Attachment, Communication, and Self-regulation - Stephen Porges

12) Book: Waking the Tiger - Peter E. Levine